SHAPING UP:

THE COMPLETE GUIDE TO A CUSTOMIZED WEIGHT TRAINING PROGRAM FOR MEN AND WOMEN

SHAPING UP:

THE COMPLETE GUIDE TO A CUSTOMIZED WEIGHT TRAINING PROGRAM FOR MEN AND WOMEN

By *GEORGE MAZZEI*

Illustrated by Ron DiScenza

BALLANTINE BOOKS • NEW YORK

Some of the material used in this book appeared in altered form in articles for *GQ*, *Playboy*, and *Los Angeles* magazines.

Library of Congress Catalog Card Number: 80-69731

ISBN 0-345-29471-8

Designed by Michaelis/Carpelis Design Associates

Manufactured in the United States of America

First Ballantine Books Edition: May 1981

10 9 8 7 6 5 4 3 2 1

Illustrations by Ron DiScenza
Cover photograph: Anthony Lowe
Cover Design: James R. Harris
Location Photograph: The New York Health & Racquet Club

ACKNOWLEDGMENTS

The following people provided the information and advice that formed the basis of the program in this book. We thank them for their cooperation and availability, especially during the research for this project but also for their help over the years.

TOM ORR, owner/manager, *Profile Fitness Center for Men,* New York City

STEVE LAITMAN, owner/manager, *Profile for Women,* New York City

AL McCLERREN, owner/manager, *The Fitness Exchange,* Houston, Dallas

ED MARIS, owner, JOHN BLAIR and GEORG CHASTAIN, managers, *The Nautilus Bodycenter* gyms, New York City, Los Angeles, San Francisco

DR. ANITA COLUMBU, D.C., and DR. FRANCO COLUMBU, D.C., husband and wife team of weight lifters and chiropractors. Franco Columbu is also winner of Mr. World, Mr. Universe, and Mr. Olympia awards, and is a World Powerlifting Champion.

JOSEPH ROTTENBURGER, masseur to five U.S. Presidents and former participant in Olympic Games, New York City

EARL BEELER, teacher and consultant of stretching exercises, New York City

ED FARNHAM, *Nautilus Sports/Medical Industries,* Deland, Florida

DONALD E. DICKENSON, Ph.D., nutritionist, and GARYX ZIMMERMAN, D.C., chiropractor, *A Health Affair* nutritional clinic, Los Angeles

SPECIAL THANKS

To *Charles Hix,* author of *Looking Good,* for constant advice and discussion while I wrote this book.

To *Jack Haber,* editor of *GQ* magazine (*Gentlemen's Quarterly*), for getting me into writing about such things.

To *Roger Sharpe,* managing editor of *GQ,* very special thanks.

To *James Duncan,* for his valuable suggestions.

THIS BOOK IS FOR ROGER SHARPE

CONTENTS

STARTING OUT

A friend of mine who has a penchant for saving money came to me a few years ago and asked me to help him get into shape. I suggested that he buy a membership at a gym. He told me that even if he joined a gym, he wouldn't know what to do when he got there. Instead, he proposed that I supervise his makeover and write it up for *GQ* magazine, where I was working at the time. The idea was, of course, too good to pass up. As he was eager to be a Willing Victim, I set up a makeshift shaping-up program off the top of my head—including a strange eating program that involved having popcorn three times a week to fend off hunger pangs.

I still don't know why, but it worked. In three months he was in shape, nicely muscled, aglow with new energy, and ready for the showroom. We had "before" and "after" shots, a story that was a hit with the readers, and a New Man. Or so we thought. The problem was that he dropped out of the program as soon as I did (I hadn't planned to make his self-image my career). In about the time it took to shape him up, he returned to the form he was in when I found him.

This is a common problem. Most people don't know what to do on their own in a gym. The desire to get in shape is there, but the knowledge is not. A lot of people are joining gyms and health clubs these days—more than ever before. Unfortunately, many of these men and women are letting their memberships lapse very soon afterward. The usual reason is that they are unable to keep up a gym program without professional advice and help, which most health clubs do not provide.

It is true that the number of health clubs that offer the "mother hen" approach to their members is growing. These clubs are highly successful, and their membership-dropout rate is almost nil. One club even has a waiting list of people who want to join as soon as there is room on the roster. Since you obviously don't want to wait until the tide turns completely and all health clubs provide constant, expert supervision to hone you into shape, you will have to become your own expert and do the job yourself.

The book you are holding supplies the guidance you need to (a) find a health club, (b) set up your own exercise program, (c) *stay in shape* once you have reached your goals, and (d) implement a nutritional program to back up the exercises. We like to think of it as a manual that will carry you through from your first day at the gym to the time when you do not have to do so much anymore.

The information contained here is not based on passing fads or "styles" of exercise. It is meant to be valid for as long as possible in this time of new discoveries and research. We have consulted a variety of sources—physical fitness experts and nutritional mavens—to arrive at a shaping-up program based on the most advanced techniques available today. This is not a crash program; it is not anybody's special system to fitness. It is simply a solid, effective approach that will help you get in shape in a reasonably brief period of time and stay that way for the rest of your life.

Because any exercise program requires you to have a working knowledge of the equipment and places you will use during your workouts, we have included some chapters on how to choose a gym that suits you, how to equip yourself if you want to work out at home, and how to establish a regimen of basic stretching exercises that will enhance your gym work. There is also a chapter on Nautilus, that unique system of weight lifting, and a section on how to use the Nautilus machines at your gym.

The nutritional section does not offer a temporary diet, but an eating plan that you can maintain permanently. It will provide the amounts of food necessary for health, energy, and personal pleasure, while bolstering your shaping-up program. Because it is not a temporary diet, its purpose is to serve the type of lifestyle you are likely to lead outside the gym as well.

SHAPING UP:

THE COMPLETE GUIDE TO A CUSTOMIZED WEIGHT TRAINING PROGRAM FOR MEN AND WOMEN

FITNESS FACT FINDING

Most people can start a shaping-up program at a gym without a special physical checkup. They are healthy; their bodies will stand up to the rigors of the work required to go from flab to firm; they have no special medical or health problems. Some gyms run their own health tests to uncover any obvious problems that might be aggravated by a sudden burst of exercise, and ask if you have a history of medical problems—particularly heart disease—that might limit your activities in the gym.

Blood-pressure tests are becoming routine at many gyms. The purpose of this test is not to eliminate you from the gym, but to record changes in blood pressure as you progress through your program. If the blood-pressure reading is too far off normal, the health club may recommend a medical checkup from a doctor.

Anyone over the age of thirty-five should get a medical checkup prior to embarking on a shaping-up program. Although it is not unusual for anyone over the age of 35 to begin to work out regularly, the risk of having a heart attack is sharply increased for this age group. Some gyms will not accept new members who weigh over 250 pounds (except for athletes, bodybuilders, and obviously nonobese people). They require that the applicant lose a certain amount of weight before joining, as heavier people are thought to be more prone to heart attacks.

While it is not likely that a gradual exercise program will bring on a heart attack, it is best to have your doctor's recommendations before getting involved in a gym program if you have a history of heart disease. And if you maintain a fairly high-powered lifestyle and are under a lot of tension and pressure, consultation with a doctor is also strongly advised.

Testing Clinics

The new medical "thing" for exercise addicts these days is the stress-testing clinic, which provides a total physical checkout to tell you all about how your body will—or can be expected to—respond to any kind of rigorous exercise program. Since these clinics give you an accurate assessment of your present state of fitness as well as a direction to take for the future, they offer a very valuable service.

How do you know if you should be tested in such a clinic? Older people—meaning over fifty—who want to start an exercise program should seriously consider it. Younger people who have never had any serious health problems may find the test results enlightening and may learn something about healthful exercise, but these tests are not necessary for them. Nevertheless, the tests and their resultant advice can be extremely important to anyone who is setting up his or her self-supervised exercise program.

The three basic areas usually covered at these clinics include aerobic fitness, which tells you the capacities of your heart and lungs; muscle strength and flexibility, which can help you gauge your weight-lifting needs; and body fat, which can guide you in determining how much you need to lose and what kind of diet to follow.

Many major cities today have athletic health-testing clinics. Local medical societies should be able to direct you; the local heart association may have pertinent information; your own doctor would be able to put you on the track; some hospitals have set up these types of clinics within their own facilities. Certain magazines that cater to runners and amateur athletes may also provide this information.

In general, a battery of tests can cost anywhere from $300 to $500, including the tests themselves and the consultations with doctors and other specialists involved. Recommendations usually encompass an interpretation of the tests to let you know how much exercise you can or cannot handle. You may need significantly more exercise than you thought you wanted; you may find that your health is not up to what you planned on doing. The specialists may offer advice on how to improve your health so that you can get into a full-scale program.

Aerobic Fitness

Most medical people gauge fitness by the body's ability to consume and utilize oxygen. The heart and lungs must be in a healthy condition to maintain this function efficiently. Almost all exercise systems can help improve the ability of the heart and lungs to deal with oxygen, but certain exercises are better for this aspect of fitness than others. Weight training is not considered to be an efficient method for obtaining aerobic improvement. This does not mean that weight training provides no cardiovascular exercise. Rather, the mechanics of preparing weights for lifting, and the normal waiting periods involved in moving from one set of weights to another in a normally crowded gym, make it impossible to sustain the high level of continuous, strenuous heart and lung activity that would provide meaningful aerobic exercise.

During weight training, your heart is exercised in short, rapid bursts, then slows down between sets of exercise. Deep, sustained lung activity is negligible during weight-lifting sessions. The heavy breathing and increased heartbeat caused by weight-lifting exercises usually last only a few minutes at a time. Two things, however, should be borne in mind:

■ Many bodybuilders who engage mainly in weight training have developed a high state of aerobic fitness through that type of exercise.

■ Nautilus Sports/Medical Industries, testing its own unique system of weight-lifting machines, has shown that it is possible, under controlled conditions, to achieve meaningful aerobic exercise while performing a weight-training program.

Does this make the short bursts of cardiovascular activity useless? The answer is no. You do obtain limited health benefits from them. At this point we would not recommend weight training as a substitute for aerobic exercise, but it would be misleading to claim that there is *no* heart and lung improvement through weight lifting.

The only way to gauge whether weight training is providing heart and lung exercise is to be tested before you begin your program and six months later. A typical test of heart and lung capacity at a medical/athletic testing clinic includes the following:

■ *An electrocardiogram.* This records the electrical impulses of the heart to see if it is working efficiently, or if any aberrations or malfunctions are evident.

■ *A treadmill test.* You are placed on a moving treadmill and asked to keep pace with the speed of the belt beneath your feet. Your arm is hooked to a blood-pressure apparatus; your nose is clipped closed so you can't breathe through the nasal passages; a plastic mouthpiece—through which you do breathe—helps record the way you utilize oxygen as you breathe in and out. If you are not able to utilize oxygen properly, your legs will begin to ache and will give out early during your "run" on the treadmill.

If the results are not up to the normal fitness standards for your age and sex, the clinic will recommend an exercise plan to help improve the state of your aerobic fitness. It may be one as simple as walking briskly several times a week, or it may be a full-fledged running, swimming, or cycling program. The clinic will also indicate whether you should avoid certain types of activity until your fitness condition improves.

Muscle Strength

The shape, strength, and tone of your muscles are interrelated. Muscle size is usually an indicator of muscle strength. However, some bodybuilders increase the size of their muscles through steroids but do not always obtain the strength that should match that size.

Muscle strength will contribute to your body's state of health, good feeling, and energy level. Muscles that are strong and taut remain young longer than those that do not get much work. When you are developed, you use less energy in your daily routine. You tire less easily and conserve energy for your bodily functions, which are then enhanced. The outcome is less psychological tension, better general health, and possibly a longer life span.

Typical strength tests at a clinic would involve:

■ *Resistance exercises,* timed and paced to test the strength of the arms and legs. These tests will also indicate any serious strength imbalances between the right and the left sides of the body. One side is usually stronger than the other, but some people may have had a childhood disease or an accident which has caused some muscles to weaken or atrophy. Muscle strength is tested by the kind of resistance you would encounter when lifting weights.

■ *Flexibility* of muscles is a more important test than that of strength. You can get along with weaker muscles, but stiffness, shortness of muscle fibers and tendons, and the inability to bend freely in all directions have a negative effect on overall fitness and are often associated with hypertension. Some people are genetically unable to perform certain stretching routines. In these cases there is no problem, but you should try to improve your ability to stretch as much as possible. Tests for muscle flexibility include toe-touching and certain bending and reaching movements similar to the stretching exercises in Chapter 10, "Stretching Out."

Body Fat

Measuring body fat is helpful in determining whether a person should undertake a weight-loss program. For many years the height/weight ratio was the only standard by which a person was considered too fat. An "average" man of 5 feet 10 inches was supposed to weigh in at 165 pounds, with no regard for his musculature and physical structure. If he was 5 pounds over, he was considered overweight. We now have a much more accurate method for measuring obesity: the body-fat percentage. Excess body fat is determined by measuring both the fat tissue in your body and how much of your total body weight is comprised of fat.

The simplest way to do this is with calipers, an instrument that resembles a pair of ice tongs. The two caliper tips are used to measure a fold of skin pulled away from the body at certain points. Chapter 12 in this book, "Eating All the Way," shows how to apply body-fat calipers.

Stress clinics use a dunking cage. Your body is weighed underwater for an accurate assessment of body-fat ratios. If the calipers are handled properly, they can provide as accurate a measurement as the dunking cage.

What are the guidelines? An average male would probably find himself at healthy body-fat levels at anywhere from 12 to 16 percent; a woman can carry up to about 26 percent body fat and still be in fine shape. Athletes—male and female—may get their body fat stripped down to 8 or 10 percent.

For weight lifters—women included—body fat acts as a "mask" for muscle definition. You may have excellent development, but a layer of fat will prevent you from seeing your true muscle definition. It is not considered unhealthy to keep body fat stripped down to a minimum, since its absence is usually caused by intense exercise. Low body fat becomes unhealthy when it is a result of undereating. Excess body fat can be unhealthy, drain your energy, and cut down on general mental sharpness even when you are not particularly fat—just carrying more than you need.

Blood Tests

A series of blood tests will also be given at the stress clinic. The most important things these tests measure are the levels of fat and cholesterol in the blood. Some clinics also test for other diseases, including venereal disease, since infections can debilitate you for an exercise program.

It should be noted here that all tests are based on national averages as the norms for certain states of fitness and health. Since the national norms may not actually represent a healthy level, that possibility should be taken into consideration. Unfortunately, most clinics do not tell you this. If you are within the norm, say, for cholesterol levels in the blood, the clinics will provide the impression that you are at a healthy level. You may want to inquire further whether you should bring some of your fitness levels either above or below the national norms.

FINDING A GYM

How to Choose a Health Club

There are two ways to choose a gym or health club. You can join the one whose name you are most familiar with. Or you can shop around until you find the one that best suits your needs, personality, and lifestyle. Either way, you will find a gym where you can work out. Either way, you will have the use of the equipment, showers, and lockers.

But a gym is something more. It represents a commitment. You will, unavoidably, be cast into some sort of relationship with the people who work there as well as with the other members. Therefore, it is best to find a place that you will want to frequent over a period of years, that you can call home.

Most of the trappings at the "superspas" may seem superfluous, just so much glitter to draw you in. Even in the simpler clubs the carpets, mirrors, and gleaming tiled locker rooms may strike you as unnecessary for a place in which to exercise. Don't underestimate their importance. The psychological picture of success, plus the excitement of starting a new program, is a great boost right at the start.

The way you react to the health club and the people there will have a strong effect on your attitude during the months to follow. Working out at a gym is a rather intimate social activity. You are displaying your body, all of your physical strengths and weaknesses, in front of your peers. Your physical prowess is on the line.

When you join a gym, you are, in a sense, "purchasing" it. All the facilities are yours to use whenever you wish. Usually there is no time limit to how long you can stay there. The health club can become a familiar, homelike place where you may come and go as you please.

Shopping Around

The first thing you should look for when considering a health club is the flexibility of hours. Some clubs are run on a coed basis. This may be good if you and your mate want to get a special "couples" discount, but it is not good if men are limited to Monday-Wednesday-Friday and women get the alternate days. Some clubs—very few, unfortunately—have truly coed facilities where men and women use the exercise rooms at the same time. Only the showers and dressing rooms are separate.

Most health clubs open very early in the morning to accommodate before-work clients and close late enough at night to enable the overworked executive to get in his time at the weights. Smaller gyms catering to serious bodybuilders and athletes may not have a wide range of available hours, but some provide keys to members who want to use the equipment after closing time.

Some clubs offer less expensive memberships if you partake of the facilities only during slow hours. For people who do not work from nine to five and can attend the gym when it is not crowded, this split-time type of arrangement may be worthwhile. Usually it will not interfere with your regimen and can often be an asset, since it provides better self-discipline and helps condition your body to working out at a particular hour. A psychological "clock" takes hold, and your muscles become primed at, say, 3 P.M. each workout day.

In general, it is best to join a club that is either all-male or all-female and allows you to use it at your convenience. You may not always be able to adhere to a split-week schedule during the course of your membership. If you run into too many days when you cannot go to the gym, your program will begin to disintegrate and you will lose ground—and, eventually, the interest in working out.

Is the gym oversold on memberships? If there are too many members for the amount of equipment, this may create a negative attitude about going to the gym. You may have to wait too long between exercises, or you may feel pressured by people waiting for you to finish and therefore not do all the work you should. A well-stocked gym will have enough equipment so that this situation does not happen as a matter of course. And instructors should be on hand as well, to see that the traffic moves smoothly.

When checking out equipment, count the number of same-size weights available. Make arrangements to visit the club during the hours you plan to use it to see how the crowd is handled. If a gym is understocked on equipment, you will run into delays even when the place is not crowded. It is more effective to run through your exercises at a fairly brisk pace; if you are kept waiting an inordinate amount of time between each exercise, your overall program will be hindered. In order to get in and out of the gym quickly, you should join a club that can reasonably be expected to accommodate your patterns most of the time.

Equipment Checklist

■ *Exercise devices.* The club should provide a full complement of free weights for your use, covering a wide range of barbells and two or more of each weight class. Some gyms have the type of barbells with replaceable weights, but newer equipment often includes bars with permanent weights. There should also be a full range of dumbbells, including 5-pounders for calisthenics and warm-ups. Weighted machines and machines that work with pulleys should also be provided, even though they often duplicate the function of the free weights.

■ *Exercise cycles* are standard equipment at most health clubs. They can act as aerobic machines for cardiovascular workouts or as warm-up machines prior to your weight workouts. To be an effective aerobics device, an exercise cycle must provide accurate meters and resistance adjustments. If the cycles in your gym do not perform properly, it is best to avoid them altogether. If they are performing well, ask the instructor to show you how to set them for a workout, since each brand has its own peculiarities.

■ *Rowing machines* are in the same class, although both rowing and cycling provide excellent aerobic workouts when performed properly.

■ *Pools.* Very few clubs in cities are able to provide space for swimming pools (or jogging tracks), but if your club has one, it is a definite plus. The swimming pool, however, should be large enough for meaningful swimming exercise, not be merely a pretty blue lagoon.

■ *Labels.* Some gyms have signs over their equipment to indicate what type of exercise is performed on each one. This is very helpful to the newcomer, who may not know which piece of equipment is appropriate to his own level of development.

■ *Mirrors.* These are important to everyone, surprisingly. Proper form—the way you move when you are lifting weights—is extremely important in muscle building. You should watch yourself in the mirror when doing your exercises to be sure you are performing them correctly.

■ *Saunas, steam rooms, and whirlpools* are *not* necessary to a shaping-up program, but they are desirable. If your club does not have these items—and this is unlikely—remember that they are not essential to a full-complement exercise program, even though they have become closely identified with gyms. They are pleasant frills.

■ *Mats.* Exercise mats are useful, sometimes necessary. They enable you to do certain calisthenic exercises safely, and aid in stretching and yoga. Clubs that have lush carpeting often do not include mats.

■ *Grips.* Leather or rubber grips are desirable when using steel barbells in order to protect the hands from calluses and blisters. Lifting with bare hands can sometimes cause excessive soreness and stiffness in the palms until you toughen up.

■ *Rest areas.* There should be a place to cool down or rest if you have unwittingly overdone your workout or stayed too long in the whirlpool.

■ *Massage.* Some clubs provide a resident masseur, who serves members at a reduced fee. Massage can enhance your shaping-up program, help offset strains and cramps, and aid muscle flexibility. If your club has a masseur—and you have the time and the money—it is a strong point for the establishment.

■ *Towels and soap* should be provided by the club. But the theft of towels and the expense of laundering sometimes make this unfeasible. Hot and cold water, and strong water pressure for relaxing muscles after a workout, are very much an important part of your day at the gym.

■ *Sun rooms, decks,* and the like are sybaritic items. If you want them and the club has them, fine. If not, don't pass up a superior health club because these things are missing.

The "Others"

A minor but important consideration when selecting a health club is to feel comfortable with its clientele. Some clubs have a large number of retired businessmen who use the place more or less as a forum. Other clubs have a family atmosphere. Some have tried the coed approach—men and women exercising together—and found it to be very successful, but you may hate the idea. Still others have a mostly gay clientele, and usually will tell new applicants that such is the case. And some clubs attract bodybuilders who tend to live in the gym many hours each day, passing steroids and making smaller men feel even smaller.

It is important for you to feel comfortable with the other members, since you will be participating in a fairly intimate activity and will have to share the equipment at least half the time. If you seek a strictly business approach to gym work, a large luxury spa, with divergent activities and personalities, may sap your willpower. If you like a gym that doesn't *smell* like a gym, choose the spa arrangement. If you don't like show-biz types, don't join a club in the middle of Hollywood.

The way to find out which is best for you is to make a trial visit to the club and ask point-blank what kind of people are already there. Do this before you sign up. Remember, you are going to have to *like* being in this place three times a week. If you have to fight your feelings about the other members, this may interfere with your mental attitude and inhibit your visits to the gym.

Signing Up

Health-club contracts are not just formalities. They are serious legal agreements and should be read carefully.

What kind of financial agreement is in the contract? Some clubs make specific provisions so that you can recoup some of your money if you must give up your membership for certain valid reasons. If you are suddenly transferred to another town, you may be able to sell the remaining time on your membership. Some clubs have 30-day memberships so that you can see if they will be suitable for your needs. Other clubs offer three- or six-month memberships as inducements to join, after which you can extend your membership, if you wish, by adding that fee to a full amount. All clubs should offer a three-day grace period to enable a new member to change his or her mind.

Although this question does come up, there is no obligation, legal or moral, for a club to refund a prorated amount of money to anyone who decides to quit the gym before his or her time is up. A change of heart is your own responsibility. The only reason to expect such a refund is if the club has failed to live up to its agreement. So be sure you know what you want before you write a check.

Sometimes a club will presell contracts prior to completion of the facilities. In this case the club will delay the start of the contract and date your membership from the day when full facilities are operational, or it will refund your money. In the past, some clubs have not made either arrangement, and members have lost their money. This situation doesn't arise often, but if you are contracting with an unfinished club, withhold your money until you can use the facilities.

How much is a fair membership fee? Fees for first-time members can range from around $200 all the way up to $500. Nautilus gyms cost more than regular gyms because the equipment is more expensive. Some clubs offer large staffs and services, and these must be paid for. Large chains can sometimes afford to charge very low annual fees—such as $200. Before you decide, ask about renewal rates. Often these second-year fees are so much smaller than an expensive first-year fee that the savings over the following years make it all worthwhile for you.

Find out if you are able to use gyms in other towns you may visit. Some clubs, though not part of a chain, have reciprocal agreements with friendly clubs in other cities as a service to their members. If you live in New York, for example, and frequently travel to Houston or Los Angeles, it would be advantageous to join a club that has reciprocal agreements. If it doesn't, ask for a clause that enables you to "freeze" your membership when you have to travel for an extended period of time. This will save you money, and many clubs are amenable to such an arrangement.

If you do travel a great deal as a matter of course, it is best to join a health club that is part of a large chain, even if you are not overly impressed with the facilities. Or join the YMCA/YWCA, which is almost certain to have a gym in any city you are in. In this way you can keep up your program wherever you go and not lose money on your membership.

Summing Up

A health-club contract should provide the following:

■ Full use of facilities during all open hours.

■ A time-freeze clause enabling you to go on vacation and not lose time on the membership. A "sick" clause in case you contract a serious disease that disables you for an extended length of time.

■ A resell clause, allowing you to sell the remaining time on your membership if you must give it up for a valid reason—such as transferring to another town, or an incapacity. A valid reason is usually *not* that you have decided you don't want to work out anymore, although there are some clubs that will agree to this.

■ An agreement to refund your fee or relocate you to another club if the gym must close for any reason.

Surviving Your First Day

A first visit to a gym is nobody's idea of a good time. You may feel intimidated. With the passage of time, however, you'll realize that most of your fears are unjustified. Every gym has a cross-section of members: most in good shape, some in top form, others in need of definite help. But remember that they all had first days, too. In addition, everyone at a gym is so involved in his or her workout and development that your own awkwardness and less-than-ideal physical condition won't be noticed. Relax and become familiar with your surroundings.

Instructors are there to help, not to hinder. They'll ask if you've had any previous gym experience, then proceed to guide you around the equipment. No matter how much you already know, ask an instructor to tell you what all the equipment is used for so that you have the gym's official viewpoint before you start.

The hardest part of the first day is persuading yourself to ask questions. The most common complaint that instructors express is that new members *don't* talk, and have to be second-guessed all the way. Ask questions. If you forget the answers, ask them again on later visits.

Even in the best gyms there can be a fast turnover of personnel. If you're lucky, the same person who measures you and advises you on the first day will still be there six months later—or even one month later, when you want someone to run the tape measure around your waist again. But because of the turnover rates, it is best to develop as much self-reliance as possible in learning your way around the gym.

Gym Etiquette

In an unsupervised gym, it is sometimes difficult to keep from becoming irritated by the actions of the other people. The irritations usually arise because someone is "hogging" the equipment, or staring at you throughout your workout because he is waiting for the machine you are using. Other situations also arise, and we have compiled a brief list of etiquette practices to help you and others share the equipment without resentment.

■ Do all of your exercises with a particular piece of equipment at one time. Some people like to set up a barbell at a certain weight and have it waiting for them while they alternate exercises with another piece of equipment—also set up for them. If you need to work out in this manner, then use the gym at a very slow time of day—or be prepared to reload the barbell each time so that other people can use it between your sets.

■ Conversely, do not interfere with another person's sets. It is important to be able to do several sets of exercises consecutively, which means you put down the weight for a brief period of time between each set. Some people hover like peregrine falcons to take the weights as soon as you remove your hands from them. Do not cut into a person's workout; he has the right to follow his own patterns without having his program halted by a nervous Nellie without manners. If you are the impatient type, buy your own equipment and work out at home, or use the gym at a time when you won't impose your problems on everyone else.

■ Although a gym is a nice place to socialize, don't drape your body over the benches and weight stands while you and your buddies talk business. It's intimidating to ask a group of people to vacate the equipment. The benches are for exercise. If you want to rest, do so in the lounge or steam room.

■ Never offer advice to someone who is doing an exercise in what you feel is the incorrect way. For one thing, you may be wrong. Or he or she may be exercising that way for personal reasons.

■ Remember that you and your gym-mates are in various states of fatigue from the workout. Because of this condition, you may be more easily angered by an action that you would normally laugh at or shrug off. A gym should have a positive atmosphere conducive to concentration and work, so try to keep your manners superhoned.

■ Remember to pick up after yourself in the locker room. If you use a towel, throw it into the receptacle so that other people don't have to wade through your wet towels.

■ The same rules of sharing apply in the locker room, steam room, and whirlpool as on the gym floor. Don't hog. If the whirlpool is a people soup, limit your time so that others can use it, too. Don't stand in the middle of the steam room doing stretches or noisy calisthenics when other people are around. They want to relax— safely—and your dance to Spring may be obnoxious.

■ Don't track wet feet into the dressing area. Other people may not want to get their socks wet because you like to drip-dry at the locker. The same holds true in the restrooms.

■ Don't sit nude on the locker-room benches. Put a towel down first. Others may not like the idea of sitting where you did.

■ If you carry a cosmetic counter around in your gym bag, be careful where you arrange your bottles, powders, and rubs. Not everyone may be delighted at the thought of the air being misted by your hair spray, your talcum may not be welcome, and someone who wants to tie his shoes in front of his locker may not like having to walk across the room to do it because the bench is occupied by your sweet disarray. Because a gym provides the feeling to each member that it is "his" or "her" own place, don't forget that everyone feels that way. It is, after all, still a public place and must be shared.

HOME GYM

With the world fairly bristling with shiny new health clubs, why should you want to equip yourself with weight-lifting items at home? There are several good reasons. Some people do not respond well to the social atmosphere in a gym. Your schedule may be such that it is easier for you to work out at odd times of the day. You may not live near a gym or be in town often enough to make the membership fee worthwhile. Or you may want to supplement your club workouts with sessions at home. Whatever your reason, you should decide carefully in advance how much you want to spend and what equipment will be most versatile for your home space.

Most people must limit their financial investment, and buy only barbells and free weights. The kind of setup involving weighted machines would require thousands of dollars, a commitment of a fairly large space, and regular maintenance. For anyone's basic needs, however, the initial outlay of cash is actually quite reasonable. You can equip yourself with all the necessary items for a complete beginning program that will serve you for the first year, and pay well under $150.

Barbells and weights require very little storage space, although you must have enough room to perform the exercises. If you have very low ceilings, you will have to do your overhead weight exercises sitting down, so you will need a bench as well—and a place to put it.

The bare essentials for a home gym include the following:

■ *A complete set of weights.* This includes a barbell, two dumbbells, and at least 100 pounds of weight plates of varying sizes. The equipment can be purchased as a weight set and is the least expensive item here. A barbell with vinyl weights can run about $35 and provide 110 pounds of weight plates. A stainless-steel set would cost about $70 and also provide 110 pounds of plates. The advantage of the vinyl is that it is easier on floor and rug, but the stainless-steel plates will be more durable.

A woman who is planning a home gym and does not want a barbell set should at least buy a set of lightweight dumbbells to add versatility to her setup. The minimum 110 pounds of weights that come with a barbell set should be enough to carry most people through the first year of a program. Many people will never want to develop muscle size to the point where they will need heavier weights, so this set can be seen as a lifetime investment.

■ *A bench* for pressing exercises, and for sitting or reclining workouts. The cost can be as little as $15 for a simple flat bench, although better models can run up to $95 or more with deluxe coverings and chrome legs. When choosing a bench for working out alone, you will need a weight rack as well. This will increase the price, but it is a safety feature. It also provides a place to store the barbell.

■ *A sit-up board.* If you have the space and the money, it's a good idea to invest in a sit-up board that can be adjusted to slant at various angles. This can be used for many other exercises, including back strengthening. If you can't afford it, however, look into one of the ankle-stabilizing devices that let you work out on the floor. Some people use a heavy piece of furniture for this purpose, but it isn't very comfortable against the bony insteps when you're doing sit-ups, and usually isn't low enough to enable you to keep your feet on the floor at all times.

■ *A wall pulley.* This can cost anywhere from $150 to $400, and none of them pass as a decorator's stroke of whimsy. They're ugly to look at, and require a strong wall and someone who knows how to install them securely. Shipping weight of the cheaper ones may total about 85 pounds, and they get heavier as the price rises.

■ *An exercise mat.* Unless you have thick carpeting, you should get an exercise mat for home workouts. It protects your body from bruises, pads the spine during certain exercises, and is especially needed for stretching work. A mat can be purchased at any sporting goods store for about $13 and can be used indoors and out.

If you plan to go a little more deluxe with your home gym, there are several other items that will add some class to the setup:

■ *An exercise bike.* Because of the popularity of these machines, their cost is pretty reasonable. A simple, non-deluxe model, weighing about 40 pounds altogether and with a speedometer-odometer, may cost under $125. A deluxe model with sleek styling, better resistance control, and other aerobic features can run close to $400. Some companies now make stands, so that you can use your regular bicycle as an exercise bike. The stands are available in several bicycle shops and sporting goods stores, and are good if you want to bicycle in winter but can't go anywhere.

■ *A rowing machine.* There are many styles of these machines, and most people may consider them out of their frame of reference as an exercise, although the aerobic benefits are present. Prices may start around $200. The exercise is the same as you'd get by rowing a boat, just as the bike exercise is stationary cycling. Rowing is a valid aerobic work and exercises the heart and lungs. Rowing machines, like exercise bikes, provide resistance, so you achieve meaningful work during your "row."

■ *Multistation pulley machines.* The dream gym. These may start around $900 and go up to about $1,500. If you are setting up a family affair, or getting together with some friends on this project, you may find the investment reasonable. The machines accommodate a full complement of exercises, just as does a weight-lifting machine at a health club. You will need to have free weights as well, usually, but your gym will be wonderfully sophisticated. The only negatives are that you will need a room to contain the machines and will have to know how to adjust, maintain, clean, and lubricate them. Having so many moving parts, they tend to go out of alignment. But if you can fix a bike, you can handle this.

■ *Saunas.* A small, compact steam cabinet, holding one person with his head sticking out, would run about $400 or more. A full wooden room with dry heat, measuring 4 by 6 feet, would start around $1,300 and climb to $4,000 or more for a deluxe model that can roast several friends at the same time.

■ *A treadmill.* For running in place. About the cheapest price you'll find for one of these belted runways is $300. It can get very expensive and sophisticated when the cost is about $2,000. It is good for running or walking if you don't like to leave the house.

■ *Scales.* Weight measurement is generally served adequately by a bathroom scale. Physician's-type scales, with the precision balance bar, cost about $150, new. These require periodic maintenance, since the balance goes off with use. You might find one for $10 to $15 at a garage sale.

Before making a huge investment, you should decide if you want to work out at home on a permanent basis. It is convenient to do so, but later on you may want all that a health club has to offer. Money spent on a set of barbells is always easy to recoup by resale, so that type of investment can be made without much hesitation. Even if you join a gym, you may want to use these weights for maintaining your program on a periodic basis. A set of weights is always good to have around.

WEIGHING IN AND MEASURING UP

On the day of your first workout at the gym, you'll need to go through the almost ritualistic procedure of weighing in and measuring that officially marks the start of your shaping-up program. Measuring up eliminates your illusions about your present shape and will provide concrete evidence for the future. You will not be able to kid yourself if you aren't doing the job. This procedure will be used as a basis for planning your goals and charting your progress over the next six or seven months.

How do you determine what your goals will be? This depends on what part of your body is out of shape. If, for example, your waist is comprised mostly of fat, it is clear that you will pay greater attention to how much tape measure is required in the future to run around your middle. One of your goals will then be to decrease the size and fat in this area. If you were once in shape, you can use that past measurement as the new goal for the future waist size. If you were never free of a belly, you will probably have to make a guess as to what waist size you are underneath the excess flab.

Arms and legs are generally easier. Women may want no more than a toning-up in the arm area, and may want to lose inches and firm up in the thighs. A man may want to add 2 or 3 inches to the biceps if he is underdeveloped in this area. He may want the look of rock formations in the biceps and a solid muscle line in the back of the arm.

Each of us has an ideal image, based on our own body type, of what we want to look like. It is a good idea this first day to go into the program with a "shopping list" of what changes you want to make in your body, whether they be

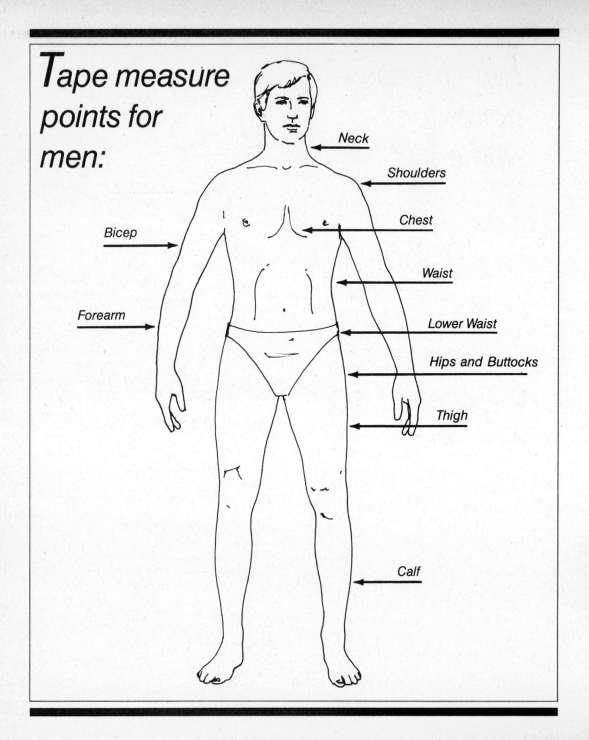

*T*ape measure points for men:

Neck

Shoulders

Chest

Waist

Bicep

Forearm

Lower Waist

Hips and Buttocks

Thigh

Calf

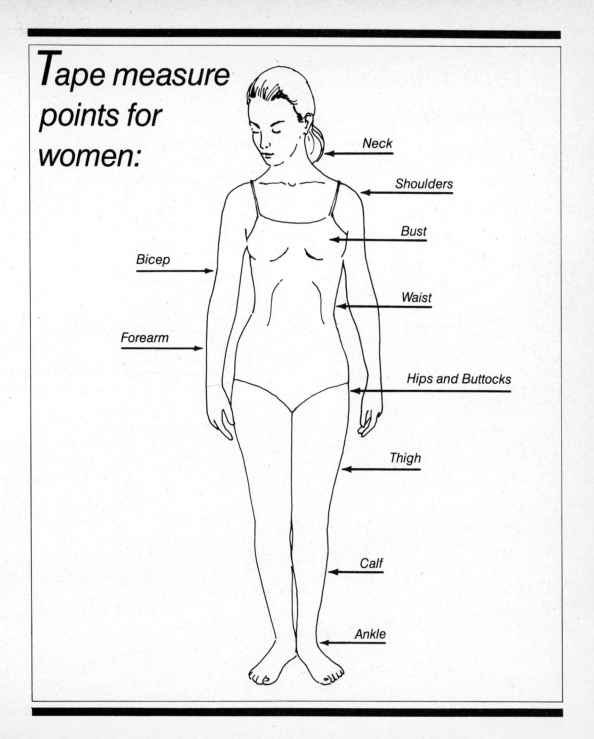

*T*ape measure points for women:

Neck

Shoulders

Bust

Bicep

Waist

Forearm

Hips and Buttocks

Thigh

Calf

Ankle

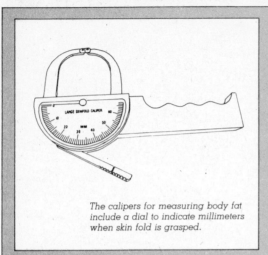

The calipers for measuring body fat include a dial to indicate millimeters when skin fold is grasped.

Records. *The instrument grasps a fold of skin and indicates the thickness in millimeters on its dial. Skin folds are measured at the tricep, at the point just below the shoulder blade, at the oblique muscle just above the hipbone, and either at the front of one of the thighs or at one of the arm biceps.*

Do not squeeze the calipers. Simply let them grasp the skin fold, and stabilize. When all four measurements are taken, add up the total millimeter readings.

The calipers that measure skin folds to determine body-fat percentages can provide an accurate assessment if they are used correctly. It is not possible to measure yourself, unless you are more agile than anyone in the Guinness Book of World

Example:

Shoulder blade	20
Tricep	9
Bicep	5
Oblique	15
Total	49

▶

losing fat, building muscle size, or just toning up the basic measurements that are there.

Tape Measure

Although it is possible to take your own measurements with a tape measure, you won't be likely to obtain an accurate reading. It is much better to have it done by someone else. It is also advisable to have the same person measure you each time in the future, since different people often read measurements differently.

Measurements must be taken while you are standing at ease, in good posture, with feet about 6 inches apart and

A scale of percentages comes with the calipers, so that you can take the total and compare it to the percentage table. This will tell you what percentage of your total body weight is accounted for by fat.

Some readings for body-fat percentages:

Millimeter Total	Body-Fat Percentages
27–29	12
30–32	13
33–35	14
36–38	15
39–41	16
42–44	17
45–47	18
48–50	19
51–55	20
71–75	25
94–100	29
188–200	38

Men carrying body-fat percentages of over 18 percent may be too fat at a "safe" level. Women can usually carry up to 26 percent body fat and be in the nonfat area. Readings of 38 percent indicate obesity. Men and women who are highly active in sports of any kind may carry as little as 8 to 10 percent body fat. It is not unhealthy for women to carry this minimal amount of body fat, unless it is caused by inadequate nutrition.

Calipers are available at most gyms these days. They can be purchased through medical supply houses and cost upward of $100. For most people they would be a frivolous purchase, and their (hopefully) temporary use would make them an unnecessary expense.

arms relaxed at your sides. Have someone wrap the tape measure around your body at the desired point, then stand and mark the tape with your finger, using one hand only. Note the point where the end of the tape meets your measurement. The tape should fit snugly around the point to be measured but should not cinch or depress the skin in any way. The result may not be precise, but you will know about how many inches there are.

These are the points to be measured:

■ *Neck:* This is the same as your collar size, taken midpoint around the widest part of the throat.

■ *Shoulders:* This takes in the full width of the shoulders, wrapping the outside of the deltoids. It is impossible to take this measurement yourself with any hope of accuracy.

[25]

- *Chest:* Lift your arms and have the tape placed around the back and over the nipples on your chest. Drop the arms and check the tape. Have this measurement taken at normal size, then expand the chest by breathing in deeply. This "inhaled" measurement is not necessary, and may be of interest only to men. It measures your ability to expand your lungs, which ability may improve during an exercise program. If you are on an aerobics program, this capacity may be improved; men on a weight-training program may find they can "blow up" their chests more than they did before the program.

- *Waist:* This is the point between the bottom of the rib cage and the top of the hipbone.

- *Lower waist:* This measures the circumference including the oblique muscles as well as the abdomen at its greatest point of protuberance. It is the place that retains body fat the longest throughout a program. When this is down to the point where you want it, you probably have met your shaping-up goals.

- *Hips and buttocks:* For women this is often considered the most important measurement, since fat collects easily here. But women should not ignore the fact that the lower waist is also a difficult area to make fat-free. A strict discipline in eating habits is vital to trimming down the hips and buttocks. The tape goes around at the hip joints to measure the midpoint of the buttocks as well.

- *Thighs:* Each thigh should be measured separately, since there is almost always a difference in size from right to left on the human body. Some people do measure out equally, but this is an exception. If you want to equalize the size of your arms and legs, you will need both measurements to gauge your development. Circle the tape about midway where the thighs swell at their fullest.

- *Calves:* Measure each at the thickest point of the musculature. Many men find that this is a difficult area to build up through weight training. It has been said that the size of the calves is determined genetically, and many bodybuilders believe it. For some people this is true, but exercise here does help build calf muscles, while diet removes fatty tissue from the area. Man or woman, if you are obese or have any fat here at all, or even at the ankles, make sure that you measure the calves. There does not seem to be any point in measuring the ankles, since no muscle growth will show in this bony area, and any fat loss will be reflected in the calves.

MEASUREMENTS

DATE						
NECK						
SHOULDERS						
CHEST OR BUST						
WAIST						
LOWER WAIST						
HIPS						
THIGHS: RIGHT/LEFT	/	/	/	/	/	/
CALVES: RIGHT/LEFT	/	/	/	/	/	/
RIGHT ARM/ CONTRACTED	/	/	/	/	/	/
LEFT ARM/ CONTRACTED	/	/	/	/	/	/
FOREARMS: RIGHT/LEFT	/	/	/	/	/	/
WEIGHT						
BODY FAT						

■ *Arms:* The front muscles are the biceps; the back of the arms are the triceps, on the upper arms above the elbows. The upper arms are measured at the thickest point while they are hanging relaxed at your sides. Each arm is measured separately. Lift the arm, "make a muscle" in the classic bodybuilder style, and measure the same point expanded. There should be about a half-inch difference in the size of the muscles relaxed and expanded. Men usually make it a weight-lifting goal to increase both the relaxed size of the arms and the ability to expand the muscle through contraction. Women may want to increase the size of the arm muscles for additional strength, they may want to shed flab here (as will most men), or they may want to tone up the arm for a better look.

■ *Forearms:* The lower arm is usually of more interest to men, from an aesthetic point of view. The slim, tapering forearm is usually preferred by women, since it makes a nice line into their smaller hands. Men generally like to see brawn here—mainly because they *can* see these muscles most easily. Women who want to lose fat should measure here, since this area, like the calves, will shed fat as the program develops. Place the tape measure at the widest point close to the elbow joint.

■ *Weighing:* It is, of course, possible to weigh yourself accurately. If you are using a balance-type scale, apply this method for weighing in: Place the weights at a reading that you know is about 15 to 20 pounds more than you weigh. Step on the scale and lower the weight gradually, by tapping it along until the gauge balances to a horizontal position. The only way to obtain accurate readings from a balancing scale is to start at a heavier point and remove weight. Do not start from a low-weight joint and move up to the balance point.

Always take measurements, readings of body fat, and weigh-ins *before* you do your workout. You will not get an accurate reading after the workout because your muscles are in a puffed-up state that will not hold past the first hour. Always measure your body during its normal relaxed state for accurate readings.

Right and Left

Because each arm and each leg is a different size and strength from its twin on the other side, the weaker limb will determine the weight you will be able to work at. This means that initially you will be favoring the weak at the expense of the strong. Later in your program you may find that the smaller arm or leg has grown enough to narrow the gap between the size of the two arms or legs. It is possible to equalize the difference, if you want, and many bodybuilders make this a definite goal in their workouts. It is accomplished by working out one arm or leg at a time, providing extra work for the smaller limb to bring it up to par.

At the earliest stages of your program, it doesn't make much sense to attempt this kind of refinement, since you do not know whether or not the muscles will equalize on their own. Later, when you have developed a notable amount of muscle definition, you will have better muscular control; then you can do extra work to bring smaller muscles up to par with their twins.

However, you may see this type of change occurring when you take the second measurement. At that time, notice the rates of growth for each limb. If they are growing at an equal rate but are not closing the gap between them, you may want to add some extra work on the smaller arm or leg from that point on. It is not necessary, ever, to close the gap if you don't want to and there isn't a significant discrepancy in size. Most people have as much as a quarter-inch difference in size between each arm. A difference as great as a half inch, however, would be noticeable, and in this case you may want to start extra work on the smaller muscles immediately. If there is a lag in growth in the weaker limb—meaning that the larger muscle is growing at a faster rate than the smaller— there may be some medical problem that should be checked out.

Problem Areas for Women

Women have a tendency to exercise only for "problem" areas, especially the hips and thighs, rather than work on overall development. This is a rather narrow-sighted approach to exercise, since you cannot separate the parts of the body from each other and expect to show good results. The upper body—the shoulders, arms, and back—must be exercised and kept in balance with the lower muscles; otherwise, severe stresses and strains will develop.

Women who plan to have children should be especially careful to strengthen the parts of the body most subject to the strains of carrying a child, particularly the back. Exercise is very important for women who are particularly "leggy" or unusually petite. By bringing the strength of the muscles into balance, you will have an easier time during pregnancy.

Women who have large breasts should remember that the pectoral muscles underneath should be strong enough to support this weight, and that the shoulder and upper-back muscles also act as supports for the area in front. By keeping these upper muscles strengthened, you will have better tone and more comfortable movement in the whole torso.

While weight lifting may not actually increase breast size, it can provide a "lift" in this area because of the stronger chest muscles underneath. It can also give a more youthful line to your profile. There are some people who claim that weight lifting increases bust size, but this is true only insofar as the breasts are lifted to a point where the measurement must be taken, so the actual circumference at that point of the chest is larger. Also, the back muscles are firmer and in better shape. When this happens, the attractiveness of the rest of the body enhances particular features, and the sight is focused more easily on how much better you look.

Timing

How often should you measure yourself? If you are measuring muscle growth, it is best to do this once every six weeks to maintain an objective, accurate picture of your development.

If you are measuring fat loss, you should do so more often, perhaps once a month, until you have lost as much as you want to. When on this type of program, the progress will move more rapidly than that for muscle growth.

Muscle growth tends to proceed at a steady pace, unlike fat loss. The muscles grow as more stress is placed on them, and they respond by building more and more tissue to meet increased demands. As soon as the demands stop, so does the growth.

Fat loss is much different. You will lose dramatically during the first week, then slow down to a steady pace. Then you may hit a plateau where there is no change for several weeks. Other changes are occurring, however, to prepare the body for future reductions. Fat loss is tied in to metabolic changes, and the body controls this systemic changeover.

If you are measuring your body fat, take a reading once every 30 days during a weight-loss program, then only periodically after you have reached your objective. If you are on a combination fat-loss/muscle-building program, things may become confusing. For example, a man's arms and chest may start shrinking in size as the fat goes, and later begin to expand again as muscle growth takes place. By measuring body fat, you will be able to know when the readings can be considered a changeover from the measurement of fat loss to that of muscle growth.

Remember that as you work with weights you are building muscles. Muscle tissue weighs *more* per ounce than fat tissue. So at a certain time you may find that you have stopped losing weight and have either leveled out or even started to gain poundage again. For this reason, people on a muscle-building or muscle-toning program cannot use the scale as the most accurate indicator of their progress. You must consider all things—the tape measurements and body-fat percentages as well.

Although it may be fun to weigh yourself every day or every week, you will obtain meaningful readings only if you record your weight at the same time that you take your other measurements. Daily weigh-ins tend to provide an average, as your weight may fluctuate around a certain point within a period of days. But comparing monthly readings will give you a true indication of weight change.

The Gym Card

At every gym the members are provided with a workout card that is kept on file there. This card records the measurements taken on the first day, and space is left for future notations. On the other side of the card is a schedule for your workouts, including what exercises to do, which weights you should lift, and how many sets and repetitions you should do. These are all dated, and again, room is left for changes to be indicated.

By providing a written record of your progress, the card will be your guide throughout your shaping-up program. You cannot cheat by pretending you are progressing when you have been sloughing off; nor drive yourself when the card clearly shows improvement. It takes the burden of proof off you. You should keep a duplicate for yourself in case your file copy is lost.

The Notebook

During the first six months of your exercise program you should keep a journal of your progress in a small notebook. In this notebook you record anything that you do or eat that affects the success or failure of your program. This serves

Bkfst: 3 eggs, 2 stoned wheat crackers. Tea/sugar.

Gym: Worked out 45 mins. Extra work on biceps. Had discussion w/ instrctr on right way to use first Nautilus machine. Ended up doing about 20 more reps than usual as he made his point, I made mine ...

Lunch: Vits/protein supplement. ½ lb. ham, pickles, crackers; 2 glasses milk. More tea, more sugar ... getting addicted again.

Afternoon: Walked home from Bloomingdale's ... 59th St. & Lex to Village with stop to see folks at GQ. My new tennies now feel real loose.

Collapse? Legs/back reee-al tired from argument at gym ... *good* tired ... Should increase intensity of workouts? Hmmm. See visual changes in waist, line of torso ... not unlike statues in museum or those bodybuilders, or maybe just kidding self. More muscle shape if not definition. Legs hard.

P.S. Measured body fat at gym, too. Still 18%. Wonder? Do they know how to use calipers? Must ask for re-test.

Dinner: Steak—huge! Zucchini, onions w/ basil. My own recipe. Tea w/ more sugar!!! And ice cream, of course.

two purposes: the concrete evidence that your plan is working—complete with data such as weight and measurements—and a commitment to that plan that takes the guesswork out of measuring your progress. Both are especially important for maintaining a positive frame of mind. It is almost impossible to see your own progress on a daily basis. The changes are gradual. If you could view yourself in a mirror only once a month, the changes would seem much more impressive. Since you will be looking at yourself in mirrors every time you work out, the notebook provides the comparison you will need. It also keeps you from deluding yourself about your eating and exercise habits.

The notebook should be a convenient size to fit into your gym bag or pocket, whichever you prefer. The smallest wire-bound notebooks—about 3 by 5 inches—are the most practical, since they slip easily into a suit-jacket pocket or a small purse and can be inconspicuous if you are recording what you ate in a restaurant.

All entries should be dated so that you can see whether you have stopped eating according to the old patterns or are still cheating occasionally. Record everything you eat and drink, when you go to the gym, and any interruptions or unusual occurrences that may affect your workouts or eating plan. If you are on an aerobics program, such as running or swimming, record when you do those workouts as well. Don't ever trust to your memory during this time.

The first entry should be of your weight and measurements, with a photo of yourself, if you like. This photographic proof is not only impressive later on—when you see how extensive the changes made from simple exercise and diet can be—but a fun thing to do. During this period of hard work and self-discipline, you will need all the fun you can get. If you are on a fat-loss program, you should record virtually every bite you eat. This is the only way you can review and eliminate bad eating habits and substitute good ones.

It is usually not necessary to maintain the notebook after the first six months, since by that time you will have made a true changeover in your mind and the new habits will have become integrated into your personality.

Another reason for record keeping is that you should never compare your own progress with that of someone else. The notebook enables you to compare yourself with yourself, in a way. Your metabolism and body function run on their own clocks. Trust your body to pace your growth according to its own safety factor. There are some cases where adjustments must be made because a program isn't working at all, but these are unusual instances, and the fault can normally be accommodated by changing the program.

In general, you will *feel* a change in muscle tone within three months of regular workouts and *see* a concrete change in muscle definition and shape after six months. By the end of the first year, you should already be at your goal and accustomed to the new you.

WARMING UP

A warm-up is a primer, a lighter version of the exercise to come that prepares your muscles, or your heart and lungs— or all of them—for the intense activity that follows. There are several reasons for this practice:

■ It readies the heart and lungs by stepping up their pace gradually. Circulation and oxygen intake are expanded, allowing an easier segue into the real workout. People doing aerobic exercises should ease in and out of them to permit the cardiovascular system to alter its normal patterns without trauma.

Doing aerobics, you can incorporate this warm-up and warm-down into the actual workout without pausing. You should spend about three to four minutes on an aerobic warm-up just before working out with weights as well, since your heart and lungs will be subjected to short, intense bursts of activity throughout these exercises.

■ A warm-up prior to weight lifting brings more muscle fibers into play for the actual workout. You will then have more strength at your disposal and will not place so much stress on your body during the exercises. The warm-up in this case is done with slightly less weight, or, if you are using light weights already, with a shorter set of repetitions.

Another factor involved in warming up is that you are fatiguing your body slightly and bringing more energy into use to handle the coming workouts.

Warming up also enables you to keep your energies on a more even keel for each day's visit to the gym, thereby counteracting the effect of "good days" and "bad days." The warm-up will wake up your system on a day when you don't feel like exercising and will lift your mood physically and psychologically by making you feel up to the task at hand. It protects you against the zeal of good days, when you are supercharged with energy and want to wipe out the gym with the weights. By using up a little of the excess energy, you can enjoy a reasonable, well-disciplined workout and not suffer a sudden pang by straining a muscle.

[35]

WARMING UP THE WEEK

The same pattern of warming up for each exercise should be applied to the whole three-day workout week. By using the "fade-in/fade-out" approach here, you can enhance your development and condition your body to maintain an even level of energies permanently. The plan goes like this:

Monday: A light workout, concentrating on control, correct form, and getting the system geared up for a week of exercise. This could be seen as a sort of warm-up day in preparation for the big one on Wednesday.

Wednesday: An intense workout to use the muscles to the limit of their ability, to reach "deep" into your strength and bring your whole muscle system to a point of momentary failure, muscle group by muscle group. This is the day for extra work, extra reps, extra sets. Show your body no mercy today.

Friday: Less intense, but a stronger workout than Monday's. Work through the fatigue or stiffness left over from Wednesday. Don't push past your limit, but leave something in reserve. This is a sort of tapering off in preparation for the two-day layoff.

Weekend: The extra day of rest guarantees that you are getting enough time to build up muscle cells, restore your strength, and come back stronger. Monday is the day of reckoning, since you will feel the new strength more dramatically after the two days off, and you can use that day to decide whether to move up in weight or reps.

This plan promotes overall health by providing your body with the varieties of intensity and rest needed for proper muscle development. You have time to get rid of periodic muscle soreness and fatigue. You have time to examine your reactions to the workouts. You have the opportunity to give proper attention to all aspects of weight lifting—form, control, and muscle growth—and can keep your spirits up because you have time to enjoy it all. The variety aspect also offsets boredom and counteracts any chance of the workouts turning into a hard grind.

Danger Points

There are four main danger points in the body for the weight lifter to safeguard against:

1. The back
2. The shoulders
3. The elbows
4. The knees

At the beginning, you should use weight-lifting equipment that minimizes strain on the body. Damage to these four areas usually comes not from the exercise itself, but from having to balance or control other muscle groups while performing it. For example, when you do the deep-knee bend with a weighted barbell, you must maintain your balance by using all the muscles of your body, when you really only want to strengthen the leg muscles. But because this exercise places stress on the back and knees, you have to keep tabs on a lot of muscles that shouldn't be involved in the exercise. It's better to choose exercises that isolate the muscles during each exercise, and equipment that gives you the most control over the weights.

You may also hurt yourself by weight lifting if:

1. You have not warmed up properly, so your muscles may not be primed to handle the weights. In this case a muscle may suddenly become strained or cramped during one of the reps.
2. You are trying to lift weights that are heavier than you can handle at your present state of development.
3. You are not using correct form.

By following the "rules" about warm-ups, choosing equipment with care, and knowing your limits, you should avoid undue pain or damage to your muscles.

SAUNA

When you think of warm-ups, your thoughts automatically turn to saunas. Reasonable as this may seem, you cannot use a sauna to warm up for a workout, although many people try to do it. It is not a healthy practice, since the heat slows down the system, congests body fluids, and decreases blood circulation and heartbeat. It also relaxes you. A true warm-up should do the opposite of these things.

While you're relaxing in the sauna—or trying to—you may be treated to a recital of someone running through his stretches before you. If you care, you might inform the person that he may be hurting himself. Although the heat helps the muscles to relax, you can tear or strain them by working out in the sauna.

Whatever sybaritic value is to be had from saunas, steam rooms, and whirlpools—as well as any health benefits—they don't have anything at all to do with working out. They are detrimental before the exercise and during the workout, and the value afterward is minimal. If you spend too long in the intense heat after a workout, it interferes with the normalizing process of the body.

There are those who still believe that sweating it out in a hot room will help them lose weight. This is flatly untrue. If you feel a little lighter after some time in the hot room, it is just an effect of the heat.

When using the steam room or sauna, do not wear clothes. Do not wear plastic, heat-trapping outfits. Allow whatever air is there to pass over your body. Do not remain in the heat longer than a few minutes at a time. Keep a wet towel handy in the dry sauna to breathe through and protect your nasal membranes.

The time to use these little hot spots is apart from your workouts. They are fine for relaxation, for certain sybaritic pleasures, and for some therapeutic purposes. But they don't do anything to shape you up.

Hauling Weights

Besides maintaining correct form during exercises, you should lift barbells carefully. When picking up a barbell from the floor—or putting it down—always bend at the knees; don't bend over and lift it stiff-legged. The former stance protects the small of the back.

When removing a barbell from a rack, grasp it from the top end, swing it down, and grasp it with the other hand near the opposite weighted end. Then carry it, evenly balanced, to the spot where you are going to use it.

When doing weight work on your back, keep your spine and body aligned. Don't turn your head to talk to someone during the exercises, as this will place stress on an area unrelated to the exercise and may cause a cramp. To check alignment, sit on the floor and let your legs rest close together comfortably. Then roll out your spine along the floor until your head is touching it. Feel your position. If one side feels off-kilter, adjust it. Eventually you'll know immediately whether your body is aligned when you lie down.

BASIC PROGRAM (MEN)

In our time, weight training has become something of a necessity. Very few of us perform the intense physical labor that strengthens muscles, so we have to work harder to counteract the softness that results from the general lack of exercise our lives create. From the start, weight lifting was meant to be used as an "aesthetic" sport. You lift weights to make your body look good. Other sports build strength, skill, stamina; weight training balances the development of the muscles for a more attractive overall shape. Although strength does result from weight training, the usual reason for doing this type of exercise is for the *look* of the muscles that results.

Weight training is not as easy as it appears. The sugar coating placed over the sport by luxury health spas tends to make it seem just like another leisure-time activity. The unvarnished truth is that weight lifting is a sport, and, like any sport, it requires exertion, concentration, willpower, and hard work. Pushing a 50-pound barbell up and down over your head 30 times, three days a week, is not easy. It is not meant to be. The only way to make your muscles grow is to push them past the limit of comfort.

It is one thing to tell you to lift weights three days a week and that in six months you will have a different kind of body. It is quite another thing for you to take a steel barbell in your hand and realize that for those six months you're going to work until your muscles can't take it anymore.

But it can be fun if you're conditioned to it and when your body instinctively knows the moves.

How the Muscles Grow

Weights themselves do not make your muscles grow. They only provide a signal to your brain that your muscles are not strong enough to handle the new intensity of work demanded of them. So your brain tells the muscles to grow more cells to provide this size and strength. As soon as that happens and your muscles are strong enough, they stop growing. That's your cue to increase the workload in the form of more weight or more intensity of work. Then the brain sends out its signal again ... and again, as you continue to put on more and more workload.

The size of a muscle indicates its strength. That means the thickness, the length and breadth, and also the number of muscle fibers that have been developed. You may see two men who appear to have the same size arms. The circumference of each man's biceps may even measure out the same. Yet one man is much stronger because his arm muscles are longer. Genetics, finally, dictates muscle development. All humans develop along similar lines, but your genes provide the distinctive shape that identifies you.

The Patterns

This program starts with exercises for the lower-body muscle groups and moves upward to the shoulders and arms. It is important always to perform the exercises in this way: large muscles first, smaller muscles last. Many people will go into a gym and start doing the exercise that is easiest for them—perhaps one for the arms—then skip to the legs. When the gym is crowded, you may be inclined to skip an exercise and come back to it, rather than wait for your turn at the weights. It is best to wait and maintain the correct sequence of muscle groups.

There are two reasons why this pattern is best for working out:

1. The hip and leg muscles, being larger than the others, have the greatest potential for developing size and strength. Since they are larger, they require more overall energy to perform the exercises.

2. The leg muscles draw much more energy to perform the workout, so you should exercise them while you're at your freshest. The smaller muscles draw progressively less energy, and since you have less to draw on as you progress through the workout, this is the logical way to go.

The sequence for exercising the body should follow this order:

1. *Buttocks:* these are the largest single muscles in the body
2. *Thighs:* quadriceps (front of thighs); hamstrings (backs)
3. *Calves:* lower-leg muscles
4. *Torso:* back; shoulders; chest (pectorals)
5. *Arms:* triceps (back of arms); biceps (front); forearms
6. *Abdominals:* (includes oblique muscles or love handles)
7. *Neck*

We run into some doubling of muscle groups here. For example, in some shoulder exercises you also bring the neck into action. Some people prefer to exercise the biceps first, even though the triceps are larger. This is acceptable. You may also exercise the backs of the thighs before the front muscles if you're waiting for a machine.

It is important to aim at a balanced development. Many men tend to concentrate only on building big shoulders, chests, and arms, and let the legs lag. They may develop problems with their backs because there is too much strength above and not enough corresponding strength below to support it. Men often focus on the biceps as the standard of their development. Biceps are traditional "macho" muscles, but, without corresponding development in the triceps, your arms will not be as strong as you'd like to think.

Do not overdevelop one part of the body. You will not look stronger, but will only point up the lack of development in other muscles. The visual effect of a man with big pecs and a weaker back is that he is carrying a chest that is too big for his strength, that is weighing him down. And, in fact, this may be true.

Also work on a sense of proportions. Some men ignore the enlargement of the calves. They may have finely developed thighs, but the lack of size in the calves cuts the strength of the image. By developing your calves, you can make the overall leg look bigger.

Think of your body as a series of pedestals, each supporting all the weight above it. This is the way the body is designed anyway. Then develop your muscles accordingly. You'll have a better overall look and less problems with your program later on.

Choosing the Weights

When deciding on how much weight you should lift for any given exercise, you're pretty much on your own. The first thing to remember is to keep your ego out of the decision. Do not try to start with weights that are too heavy for you. You will hurt yourself early on and may have to drop out of the program indefinitely.

First, try lifting a weight you can do 10 reps with comfortably. You may have to go much lower at the start. If you are a real bear, you may want to begin with more weights. Much of this depends on your native strength and previous development.

The weight should make you work to raise and lower it. If you can swing it around with no effort, it is too light to do any good. It should be heavy enough to cause you to work from the first repetition and should become progressively more difficult to raise and lower as you move through the reps. You will be doing sets of 10 repetitions, and the weight should make you really work deeply by the end of that number.

A proper initial workout will have you exerting yourself at about 50 to 60 percent of your capacity—which means you are really pushing your muscles to work at that intensity. If you find your workouts are fairly easy, you may be using too light a weight or not doing enough work with the proper weight.

The resistance of the weights against your muscles, however, should still allow you to be able to control your movements. You should feel as if the weight is difficult to move, but not to the point where you must use other parts of the body to heave it through the repetitions. The weights should be manageable—especially during the early weeks—so you can learn correct form and become conditioned to the proper ways of handling them.

Correct Form

Form follows function, and this is the basis for the correct use of the weights. There are two reasons for correct form:

■ First, to avoid damage and strain on the muscles.

■ Second, to develop the muscles in the most efficient way and obtain the greatest benefit from the exercises.

When working properly with weights, you must use smooth, even, controlled movements. Never "jerk" the weight into position, or "cheat" by heaving with the rest of your body. If you are unable to move your muscles through a complete set of exercises on their own strength alone, you are using weights that are too heavy.

Correct form for one complete repetition is this:

■ Contract the muscle to its fullest ability in a smooth, even motion. This is called the POSITIVE MOVEMENT. Use only the muscle's strength to perform it.

■ Hold the muscle in the contracted state for a beat of 1.

■ Return the muscle to its original, full-out stretch. This is called the NEGATIVE MOVEMENT. It should take about twice as long as the positive movement.

There is no rule for how long the positive and negative movements should take. At the beginning, it is best to take them slowly in order to condition your muscles to the weights and learn correct form. Also, you will be able to feel how your muscles work under the pressure of the weights. As you advance, you may shorten the time spent on each repetition.

At the onset we suggest you use beats, or clock seconds, to pace the positive and negative movements. This will condition you to use the correct form automatically later on without counting. For example, use two beats to bring the muscle into full contraction through the positive movement, hold it for one beat at full contraction, then perform the negative movement at about four beats.

Sets and Reps

The number 10 is generally accepted as the best number to determine how many repetitions make up one complete set of exercises for a muscle group. This is an average, of course. Some people give themselves a range of from 10 to 15 reps per set. When they can do 15 easily, they move up in weights; or they use this range as a general indication of how many reps they want to do in a set, depending on whether or not they want to engage in a superintense workout.

You will have days when you will feel stronger, so allowing yourself the leeway of a few reps is a good idea. This is an area that must be judged for yourself, since everyone's muscles act and respond differently. Do not become frustrated by rigid rules. If you need leeway to make your program work for you, then take it. Develop your own style. As your muscles become conditioned to weight work, you will be able to become more precise.

REVIEW OF SETS AND REPS

How many repetitions should you do per set? The answer must be determined by you. The basic recommended number is 10 reps per set, but that is only a suggestion. You may be able to go up to 15 reps before you reach muscle failure; someone else may do only 8 or 9. Some people feel you should move up in weights if you can do 15 reps, but that may not work for you. Some people can do 15 reps at 30 pounds but only get to 7 or 8 at 40 pounds. Let your own strength be your guide. Don't try to fit yourself into a general rule.

The same is true for numbers of sets. If you can do three full sets of exercises, then obviously your muscles should receive that much exercise for maximum results. If you only want to keep your muscles in tone and aren't interested in large size, then don't always push past your limit on numbers of sets.

Always aim to find your own style.

The suggested way to work out is in sets of two or three. Many people feel that three sets of reps at any given weight is a cutoff point. After you have mastered three sets, you move up in weights and go back to doing less sets of reps with this heavier resistance until you master that level.

The first set of reps should be considered a warm-up. On your first day, however, do only this one set, then get into a full workout on the next day at the gym. During the beginning days of your program you may not be able to achieve two complete sets. If you can only do, say, eight or nine reps at the end of the second set, it is not a failure. Your muscles may still be learning the moves.

Always perform the first set as a warm-up. This means using about 5 or 10 pounds less than the normal weight load, then doing the second and third sets at full weight load.

Once you are adjusted to the program, you should be able to perform a *full set of 10 to 15 repetitions on the second set.* You may not be able to do a full amount of reps on the third set, but you should try to do a complete second set.

The third set can be used as your gauge for moving up in weights. When you can perform a complete third set, it is time to increase the weights or add another set. This decision is up to you. It may be more feasible for you to add another set rather than try to handle a heavier weight load. Again, this is something only you can decide.

Muscle Failure

Muscle failure is vital to growth. What does it mean? The occurrence of muscle failure in an exercise program is an indication that you have achieved something desirable. You have *temporarily* fatigued your muscles to the point where they cannot perform one more repetition on their own strength and in correct form. When you reach that point, it is time to stop the set. You may decide to do another set after resting for a few minutes, or to go on to exercising the next muscle group.

The muscle failure is temporary. After about 30 seconds you should be able to perform more reps—perhaps another full set, or maybe only part of a set until you reach muscle failure again. Some people feel that reaching muscle failure once each workout is adequate for development. Others try to go for it again and again. Some people do not try for muscle failure at all. The muscles still develop, but more slowly.

Why does muscle failure work? Because we are sending that signal to the brain that more growth is needed at the muscle level. When you do any kind of intense physical work, the brain receives a signal to initiate the process of building more muscle cells to handle the increased stress. The brain starts this process immediately—after the first time. If you keep sending that message, the brain will keep ordering new muscle cells. When you stop doing the work, or stop increasing the weights, the brain either eliminates cells that aren't needed anymore or maintains the muscle at a strength to handle the weight load at which you've leveled off.

So you are not working for the sake of working. You are lifting these weights to send a message to the brain to order bigger muscles. You must decide for yourself how many message units you want to transmit. Some people feel that once you have sent the signal, it is pointless to send another message until the next workout. Others feel that more messages per workout result in stronger muscles. There is controversy on this subject, and we are not trying to resolve it. The only point to be made here is that, at the beginning, overdoing is often a bad practice. The learning process is more important at this point than is working yourself into the ground, and the risk of injury now is greater than later on, when you are better conditioned to this kind of work.

How Often?

There is much less doubt about how many times a week you should work out if you want to see results. You must work out at least twice a week, and preferably three times. Some people work out religiously every other day. But it's not advisable to exercise the same muscles every day.

Your body requires at least 48 hours to build up new cells and to rest. After four days your body starts losing what growth you've gained, so it is best not to let more than three days pass without a workout. If you work the same muscles every day, you will destroy tissue, not build it up.

You can exercise every day, but on alternate days you should do another type of exercise. Some bodybuilders work out on two-day programs—they do intense leg exercises on Monday, Wednesdays, and Fridays, and intense upper-body work on alternate days. But even on that kind of program the body should be permitted regular days of complete rest.

The idea of working out three days a week and resting on the weekend is ideal for the beginner. It guarantees the proper amount of exercise for muscle growth and also provides the muscles with enough rest to catch up on their growth.

Note: Although rest is essential for people who exercise at all levels, total collapse is not. You should maintain your normal schedule of activities every day without suffering undue fatigue.

Weight Handling

If your exercises are done mostly with free weights, you will have to handle the weights when moving them from storage racks to your exercise station. In some gyms, you will have to add or subtract the weights you need. It is important to treat them with some care and good sense so that you don't strain a muscle on the way to the exercise. When moving a barbell from a storage rack, grasp it close to the weight at the top end, bring it smoothly down, brace it against your body, and lift it out of the rack. Then let it down to the floor.

To lift it from the floor, bend at the knees, feet apart for a good base. Grasp the barbell with hands at a comfortable width and bring it up, using your legs and without placing stress at the small of your back.

Always lift or set down the barbell in that manner. Never try to pull the barbell up in a straight-leg position unless you are doing a specific exercise. You can easily rip a muscle or cause a painful cramp in a weak spot that may nag you for a long time afterward.

Correct Breath Control

Breath control is important when doing any exercise because it helps you do the lifting. Correct breathing is as important to exercise as correct form. Breath brings oxygen into the body and lets certain chemical processes take place during the workout. Breath control also helps you discipline yourself into a rhythm that makes the actual lifting seem easier.

Correct breathing is simple:

- *Inhale* before you start.

- *Exhale* on the positive movement.

- *Inhale* on the negative movement.

Note:

In the basic program of exercises that follows, we are providing several exercises for the same muscle groups. This does not mean that you should do all of them; choose the ones that can be done on the equipment available. If you are working out at home and have only barbells, then select the appropriate exercise for them.

Gyms stock machines which may be preferable over barbells for certain muscles, and we are including exercises for them.

Deep-Knee Bends:

thighs, buttocks

Use barbell for this one.

This exercise is one of the few that will act effectively on the gluteal muscles. It is also the most effective for fast development of the upper leg, and exercises all the muscles of the thighs and buttocks at the same time. The problem is that it places a lot of stress on the lower vertebrae of the back and on the knees. We suggest that, until you have conditioned your muscles to this exercise, you work with lighter weights or an unloaded barbell. If you can, do the other exercises for these muscles.

Movement:

■ Stand erect, feet planted about shoulder-width apart, toes pointed slightly outward.

■ Place weight across your shoulders, behind neck, and stabilize it with your hands.

■ Slowly bend your knees and let your butt sink toward the floor until you reach maximum squat position. (POSITIVE MOVEMENT)

■ Pause.

■ Return to standing position. (NEGATIVE MOVEMENT)

Note: Inhale on the way down; exhale on the way up.

Leg Press:

thighs, buttocks (alternative to deep-knee bends)

This is easier on the back and knees, but requires more flexibility. You do not need to balance your body and can focus on the muscles being exercised. There are two types of machines that can be used: One has you lying on your back; the other, sitting in a seat. We are describing the lying-down type, but otherwise the movement is done the same way.

■ Lie with feet braced up against the footboard.

■ Extend legs until they are straight, and exhale during the movement.

■ Bring knees down into chest all the way, inhaling.

■ Pause. Then extend legs again.

Note: You can do your calf, or lower-leg, exercise in this machine as well. After completing the leg presses, extend legs straight up and raise and lower the weights, using your toes.

There is a third alternative for exercising the thighs that is the easiest to perform, as well as the safest for the back and knees. Two separate exercises are required on the leg-extension machine.

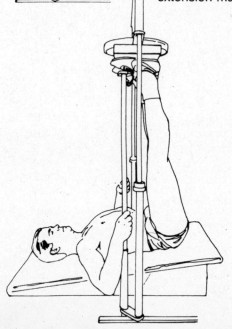

Leg Extension: for quadriceps (front of thighs)

■ Sit on edge of table and hook ankles behind lowest roller bar.

■ Grasp edges of table with hands for stability; keep spine straight.

■ Slowly extend legs straight out in front of you, exhaling.

■ Pause. Then slowly lower legs but do not let pressure of weights off them, inhaling. Immediately start next rep.

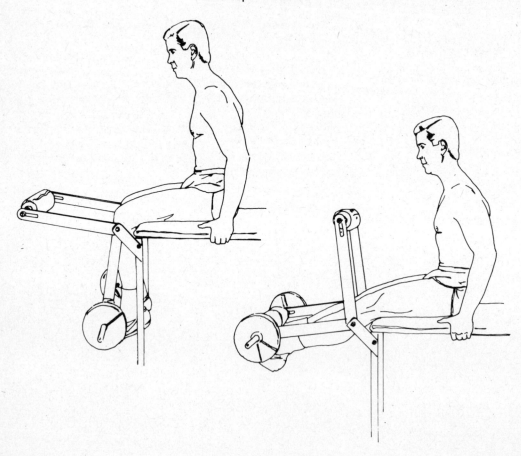

Leg Curls: for hamstrings and buttocks (backs of thighs)

- Lie face-down on table, braced on elbows.

- Press back of heels against highest roller bar.

- Slowly bring your heels in toward your buttocks as far as you can, exhaling. Arch back slightly if you need to accommodate movement.

- Pause at full contraction. Then slowly return legs to extended position, inhaling. Do not disengage weights but go immediately into next rep.

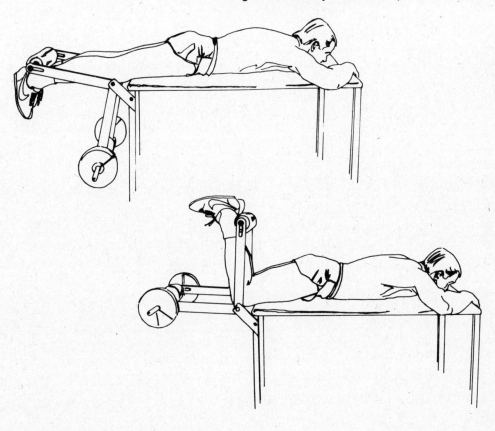

Calf Raises: for lower-leg muscles

Whether you use a barbell or a calf-raise machine, the exercise is performed the same way. When using a barbell, you can place toes on a slightly raised platform so that the heels will go lower and stretch the muscles.

■ Stand with weights against shoulders (barbell held on shoulders behind neck). Feet together.

■ Raise up on toes as high as you can, inhaling. Pause for a beat.

■ Slowly lower heels almost to floor, exhaling. Go immediately up on toes again.

Note: By keeping toes on a raised platform, you can maintain weight resistance on muscles throughout the set. By resting heels on floor, you break the resistance and allow your calves to rest each time. Keep the weight resistance on the muscles throughout the set.

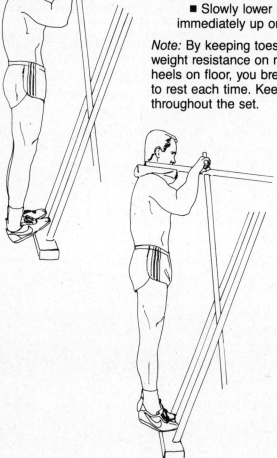

Pulldowns: for back and latissimus dorsi muscles

■ Stabilize bar of pulley with both hands and place it across your shoulders behind the neck.

■ Kneel down, legs apart, to engage the weight stack. Let your hands extend straight up, but keep weights engaged throughout the set.

■ Pull the bar down evenly—keeping it horizontal—until it touches your shoulders behind neck.

■ Pause at full contraction. Raise arms slowly to full extension above head. Immediately repeat next pulldown.

■ Inhale going up; exhale pulling down.

Bench Press: for pectorals

It is suggested that you do both this and the following exercise for the chest for a fuller range of movement. During the early part of the program you may want to do only one, but as you become stronger you will obtain better development by performing both.

- Lie on bench, supported from butt to head. Barbell is held horizontally across chest. On weight machine, position hands at about chest level. Keep elbows wide.

- Push weight straight up from chest; lock elbows.

- Pause. Return weight down almost to chest; immediately go into next rep.

- Exhale going up; inhale coming down.

Note: On this exercise, it is important to keep elbows wide to place full stress on the pectorals.

Dumbbell Presses: performed on an incline board

■ Lie back on an incline board, holding dumbbells of equal weight, one in each hand.

■ Hold the dumbbells at shoulder width, elbows wide.

■ Press the dumbbells up from your shoulders and touch them together straight out from the chest by extending arms fully.

■ Return dumbbells to original position.

■ Exhale on the extension; inhale on return.

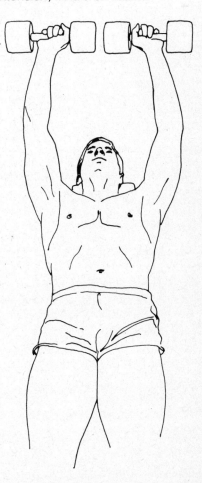

[57]

Behind-Neck Press: for shoulders, using barbell or weight-lifting machine. (You may be able to sit when using the machine.)

■ Stand with feet apart for proper support. Barbell is placed on shoulders behind neck and grasped with hands close in to shoulders.

■ Push barbell straight up evenly, keeping it horizontal, until arms are fully extended over head.

■ Pause. Then lower barbell slowly to shoulders. Go immediately into next press.

■ Exhale as you press up; inhale coming down.

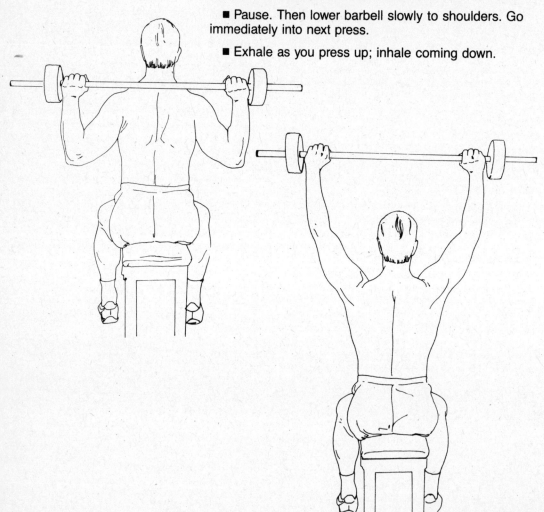

Standing Military Press: for shoulders (and chest muscles)

This can also be performed with a barbell or a weight-lifting machine. On the machine, you may be able to sit while doing it, as in the preceding exercise.

■ Stand erect, as with behind-neck press. Place bar across chest, this time with hands at shoulder width. Palms should be facing out from chest.

■ Push weight straight up until arms are fully extended and elbows locked.

■ Pause. Then lower barbell or weight to chest again. Go immediately into next rep.

■ Exhale pushing up; inhale coming down.

Bicep Curls: front of arms

There are many different positions in which to perform the bicep curl, but the principle remains the same, as does the action of the exercise. This is the only movement for exercising these muscles, no matter where you place your elbows. Remember, the elbows must remain stationary throughout the exercise. If you have access to a bicep-curl stand (see "Learning the Equipment," p. 138) it is recommended that you use it. If not, perform the curl this way:

■ Stand with feet apart about 6 to 8 inches. Hold barbell with hands facing out and arms extended down. Hands should be placed so that they come up to touch shoulders.

■ Keeping elbows in position, bring barbell in a half circle up to your chest.

■ Pause. Lower barbell until arms are fully extended again. Immediately bring them into next curl.

■ Inhale on the way down; exhale during the contraction.

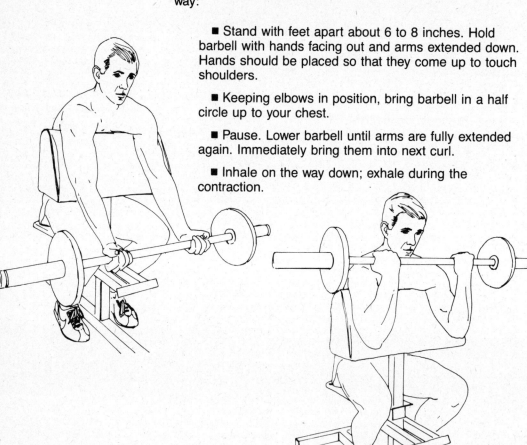

Note 1: It must be stressed that for this exercise it is important to *keep elbows stabilized.* If you can't do that with the barbell and have no curl stand, try it with dumbbells, one arm at a time, like this:

■ Hold dumbbell in one hand, arm extended down.

■ Make a fist with free hand and place the back of hand just above elbow of weighted arm to stabilize it during the exercise.

■ After completing the set, exercise the other bicep in the same manner.

Note 2: It is very easy to "cheat" during this exercise—even using a curl stand—by bringing other parts of the body into play to help heave the weights through the hard part of the set. It is important to avoid this and use the muscular strength of the bicep only during the curl. Otherwise you will slow down your development of this most visible of muscles.

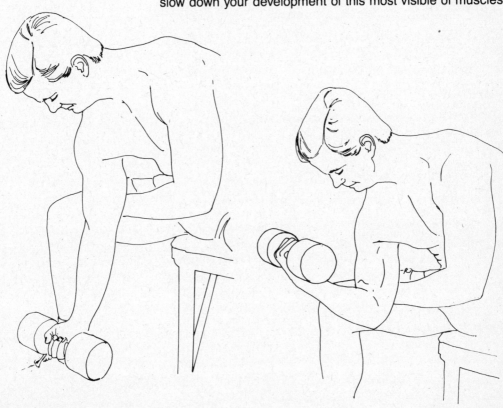

Pressdowns: for triceps (back of arms)

This is performed with a weighted pulley—the same used for the pulldown for the back and lats. We will also show the French curl, which is done with a barbell or dumbbells.

- Stand with hands close together, palms down, grasping the bar. Feet apart. Move away from machine to engage weights when holding bar at chest level.

- Keep elbows in and push straight down until arms are fully extended downward.

- Pause. Bring bar back up to chest level, keeping elbows close in to body all the way. Repeat next rep immediately..

- Inhale coming up; exhale pushing down.

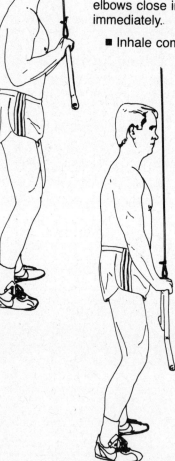

French Curls: using barbell and bench

■ Lie face-up on bench, head tilted slightly back. Hands are close together toward center of barbell.

■ Hold barbell extended above chest, elbows locked.

■ Lower barbell to forehead in POSITIVE MOVEMENT, inhaling.

■ Return arms to full extended position above chest, exhaling.

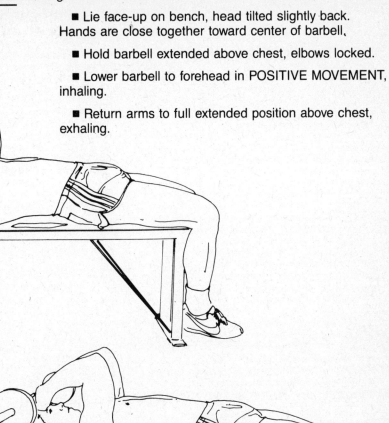

Forearm Curls: use barbell

■ Sit on bench, elbows braced on knees, palms upward, holding barbells.

■ Curl hands in toward forearms, as if trying to roll the bar into your arms.

■ Return hands to straight-out position.

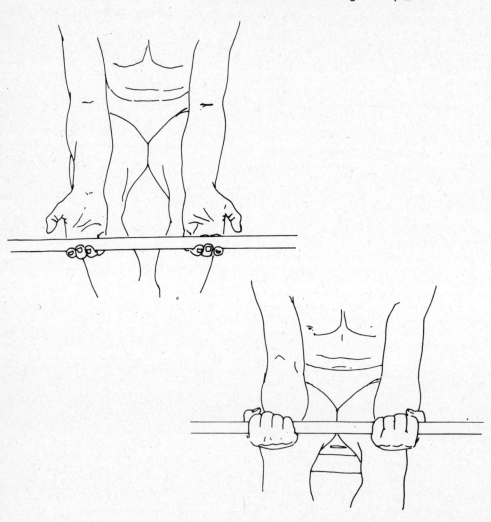

Upright Rows: for trapezius and neck

The beginner may find that the aftereffects of this exercise leave him with a rather stiff neck. If so, do stretching and elongating for a few weeks to strengthen the neck muscles, then add this exercise to your regimen. It is easy to overdo the upright row when you're starting out. Later on, however, you'll be glad you did it, because the development here makes a good complement to the shoulders and pectorals.

- Stand holding barbell at hip level, arms extended downward. Palms grasp barbell, facing inward, held straight down from shoulders.

- Keep hands close to chest, bringing barbell up to chin, exhaling.

- Lower barbell to starting position, inhaling.

Extra Shoulder Work:

The deltoid muscles, which form the round "knobs" of the shoulders, are exercised in many of the upper-body sets. However, you should add lateral raises to work them specifically, and to provide work for latissimus dorsi muscles as well.

Lateral Raises:

■ Using dumbbells, hold one in each hand, arms resting at sides. Stand erect.

■ Raise arms straight out, elbows kept locked throughout, until they make a horizontal line with shoulders.

■ Pause. Lower them *almost* to straight-down position and immediately raise them again. (This keeps weight on shoulders at all times.)

■ Exhale as you raise arms; inhale going down.

Note: You can vary this exercise by leaning forward as you do it, letting arms dangle straight down to floor rather than keeping them at your sides.

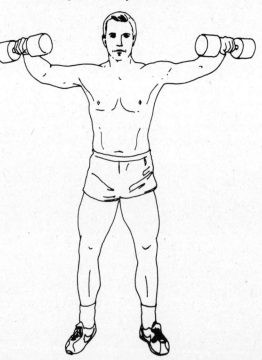

**A**bdominals: There are many effective ways to strengthen the midsection. We are presenting several here.

Twists:

This is the fastest way to pull in the abdominals and provide a slimmed-down look even if you still have fat in that area. The points to remember are to keep the hips stabilized and the back straight. Most people move the hips with the upper body and lurch forward, and therefore don't get the effect of the exercise.

■ Sit—either on the floor with legs straight out in front of you (most effective) or on a bench so that thighs are horizontal in front of you (a low stool is best here).

■ Place a wooden dowel or a steel unweighted bar across the shoulders, behind neck, and extend arms to rest hands over the bar.

■ Exhale, and twist shoulders and head to one side— all the way. Return to face front. Inhale.

■ Exhale, and twist shoulders and head to face the other side. Return to face front.

■ Repeat until abdominals are feeling it.

Note: Some people do this exercise standing up, but it is almost impossible to stabilize hips that way. It's best to do it sitting down.

Leg Raises:

If you have problems with weakness in the lower back, do not do this.

- Lie on back, body aligned, arms at sides or hands under buttocks.

- Raise both legs together to form a 90-degree angle from body.

- Lower legs *almost* to floor and immediately bring them up again.

- Exhale raising legs; inhale lowering them.

Note: Remember to concentrate on abdominals during this exercise, and do not arch back. Keep knees straight throughout.

Variation: Use the leg-lift stand if your gym has one, or a slant board, and raise legs from the floor and lower them again.

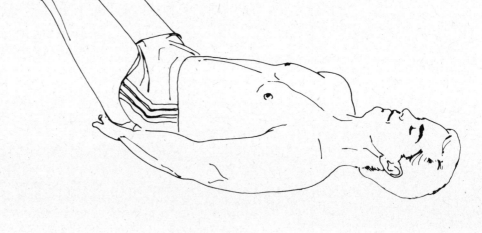

Sit-ups:

This is best for creating the "washboard effect" on the midsection.

■ Lie on a slant board, with knees bent, hands touching neck.

■ Raise upper body by curling toward knees. Do not use hands to pull up neck; use abdominal strength to achieve this.

■ Pause. Lower almost all the way back. Go immediately into next rep.

■ Inhale on way down; exhale coming up.

Note: Later you can add weights, holding them at neck level for added resistance. You can use this as another weight exercise, increasing weights and sets as you become stronger. At the start, however, the sit-up alone will develop you.

Variation: Do not go all the way up to knees, but just far enough to fully contract abdominals. Pause, go almost all the way back, then immediately enter into contraction again. This trims excess movement off the sit-up and provides greater intensity and faster muscle fatigue.

Some people do this intense sit-up lying flat on floor and stabilizing lower part by folding legs in yoga fashion. This is recommended only as an advanced technique, as it places undesirable stress on the lower back.

Learning the Moves

If you have never had any experience with weight training, do not forget that this is a new sport and you are learning it. The moves are different and new; you may move in similar ways in your daily activities, but not often. Your muscles must become conditioned to perform these strenuous movements.

Remember, too, that nothing in your daily life requires the kind of intense short bursts of exertion and strength that you will experience during a weight program. The only way to build strength is to use strength. The impact of this point does not really come home until you are involved in the actual exercise itself. Many people keep trying to do the weight lifting while trying not to expend strength. Adjust your thinking to the fact that you must put out intense effort during the exercise so that you can learn the sport more quickly.

Correct form is vital to weight training. It is more important to do less exercises correctly than to do a lot of them incorrectly. When done in the proper way, you minimize negative aftereffects such as soreness, strains, and psychological aversion to the workouts.

During the first six months, even though you will show muscle development, you must consider yourself in the learning stage. Your muscles have to become accustomed to moving and lifting in this new way. Once you teach your muscles how to control their strength and the weight resistance, there isn't much that can stop you from shaping your body any way you want it to look.

If You Don't See Quick Results

There is a possibility that, even doing things right, you may not see the results you want. Here are some reasons:

Age: Men over forty may need a longer time to shape up. Although there is no age limit to starting a gym program, the metabolism of an older man may make it harder to build muscle tissue, and the final results may be less than a twenty-year-old's doing the same work.

Fat overlay: Fat masks muscle definition. If you want to see your muscular development, you will have to strip off the excess body fat. By the way, there is no such thing as turning fat into muscle. You must lose fat through dietary means and build muscle tissue through exercise. There is no conversion from one to the other. Muscle does not turn to fat from lack of use either—it simply decreases in size.

Poor nutrition: You must eat properly to build muscle. Otherwise you will remain stagnant or even tear down muscle tissue. See Chapter 12 on nutrition.

Not enough work: After a short time, you may have responded faster than you realize and can handle more sets, even if you can't handle more weights. Or try doing other types of exercise for the same muscles to enhance the basic workout. If you want greater development, don't be afraid to branch out.

PARTNERS

There is a theory that having a buddy to work out with helps you make a success of a program. Your buddy, says the theory, will be there to cheer you on during those days when you don't want to get moving. This theory works only when the buddy is as highly motivated as you.

If he isn't, the two of you may become reasons for each other not to go to the gym. You will use the excuse that your buddy is busy, or not feeling well, and eventually you will stop the program.

If you can't do it alone, you won't be able to do it on someone else's willpower, either. You will be dependent only on your own schedule variations, your own development needs. Working out should be a private decision, and you should do it on your own.

WORKOUT CHART

EXERCISE	MUSCLE
DEEP-KNEE BEND	THIGHS
CALF RAISE	CALVES
BENCH PRESS	PECTORALS
BEHIND-NECK PRESS	SHOULDERS
MILITARY PRESS	SHOULDERS
BICEP CURL	BICEPS
FRENCH CURL	TRICEPS
FOREARM CURL	FOREARMS
LATERAL RAISE	DELTOIDS; LATISSIMUS
UPRIGHT ROWS	SHOULDERS
TWIST	ABDOMINALS
SIT-UP	ABDOMINALS
LEG RAISE	ABDOMINALS

FIRST (DATE)	SECOND (DATE)	THIRD (DATE)	FOURTH (DATE)	FIFTH (DATE)	SIXTH (DATE)
SETS REPS WT	SETS REPS WT	SETS REPS WT	SETS REPS WT	SETS REPS WT	SETS REPS WT

BASIC PROGRAM (WOMEN)

Women's gyms tend to offer more opportunities for different types of exercise than clubs catering to men only. Also, women's clubs offer much more supervision and help to their members than their male counterparts. Exercise classes are plentiful, including yoga, dance exercise, stretching, and the like. Besides that, you'll find the full complement of weights and equipment needed for muscle toning and strengthening. These extras provide women with a complete range of exercise within the health club: supervised aerobics through calisthenics classes; stretching for flexibility; weights for shape.

This trend reflects a growing awareness on the part of women that a full-spectrum, strenuous exercise program is important to looks and health. The commonest complaint from gym instructors of women's clubs is that too many members only want to do exercises that will trim the hips and thighs. There is still the lingering misconception among many women that they will lose their feminine shape if they engage in weight training or do too much exercise for the upper body. Thus, they tend to shy away from strength training. Because a woman's goal is not likely to be toward the cultivation of big muscles, the use of weights and weight-lifting equipment requires a different approach than a man will take. You will use lighter weights, and will work out in a different manner to get the best cosmetic results. It should be noted here that weights can be used for either strength or cosmetic purposes. By working out with lighter ones, you can tone

YOUR SELF-IMAGE

There is more than one type of beauty, although a glance at the popular publications and TV ads would make you think differently. Avoid cloning yourself. When deciding what you want to look like, it may be fun to remember the old French exclamation, "Oh! Quelque tu as!" which is pronounced something like, "Oh, Calcutta!" and means, more or less, "Oh, that which you have!" It is a nice way of saying that your own personal quality is what's important and attractive, not whether you're endowed like, say, Bo Derek or Farrah Fawcett.

The human body, when in shape, looks good. It is a fact of nature that when you feel good and respond to being in shape, not only are you attractive physically, but you also send out energies that let other people know how you feel about yourself. And they generally agree.

Look at what you have. Decide what you want to look like further along in the program. As you shape up, you'll see the direction you're heading in and can dress and move—and plan—accordingly. Remember to shape up for yourself, for your own self-esteem, and for your own health and comfort. Nature will take care of the rest.

■

your muscles and bring your overall figure to the silhouette you want.

What about the new crop of female bodybuilders? Close scrutiny reveals that their muscles are not outlandishly oversized. The reason one can see their muscle definition is because they have stripped away all body fat and tensed their muscles—much the same as a ballet dancer. Even then, the lines of their bodies are definitely female. Nor is their development any more unusual than that of a woman athlete. For you to achieve that kind of development, you would have to use heavy weights and follow the program for men instead of the program outlined in this chapter.

Starting Out

As a warm-up, it is suggested that you jump rope or take a stationary spin on an exercise cycle for two or three minutes. This will exercise the heart and lungs and make it easier to handle the exertions of the subsequent exercises. If you are on an actual aerobics plan, you should keep it separate from the weight program. Do your aerobics on alternate days, or take a rest period between the weights and the aerobics if you do them on the same day. Remember that weight training requires a lot of energy, and you may be too tired to do both programs back to back.

Weighting

How heavy should your weights be? The first thing to remember is that it is impossible to increase muscle size by working with weights that are too light for your strength. That may be just fine with you, but there will be a slight increase in muscle size even if you are only toning the muscles. Most of the gym work you do will be of the weighted calisthenic type, since this program is not geared to building big muscles.

It would be a good idea, however, to devote several times a month to working out extra strenuously with the weights, perhaps putting on some heavier poundage, in order to enhance your strength. But when starting out—and especially if you haven't done any exercise in recent years—the recommendation is to begin with the lightest weights.

Before attempting to use any weights, go through the motions without them, using an unloaded barbell or the weighted pulley equipment at its lowest setting. The reason for this is simple: All weight equipment was originally designed to correspond to a man's strength. A very light weight for a man may be too heavy for many women, although a great number have a lot of strength in their muscles. It is very important at the start to *know* your strength limits and set your weights accordingly. The lowest weight you'll probably find are dumbbells of 3 or 5 pounds each. A barbell unloaded weighs about 12 or 12½ pounds. The lightest weight plates made are 2½-pounders, so you would have to work out with loaded barbells at about 17 pounds or more.

It may happen that the lightest weights available are too heavy for you to use for some of the exercises. In this event, you should strengthen those muscles with stretching and calisthenics for several weeks until you get to the point where you can handle the weights. If you are that low on strength in some muscles, it probably is advisable to do a certain amount of strength training in those areas until you reach a higher level of strength. Here even the lightest weights would cause you to build some muscle tissue until you develop past the point where the weights are too heavy for you.

Correct Form

Correct form is as important here as if you were using heavy weights for muscle growth. When you are working with lighter weights for the purpose of increasing muscle tone, you can do faster, more frequent repetitions. If you want to increase muscle size and strength, follow the same advice presented in the chapter entitled "Basic Program (Men)," page 40.

The movements used for working with weights must be smooth, flowing, and evenly controlled.

■ Start with the muscle to be exercised fully extended. Inhale.

■ Bring the muscle into a state of full contraction engaging the weights. Exhale all the way.

■ Pause briefly.

■ Return the muscle to a state of full extension, inhaling. Do not let the muscles relax at this point, but go immediately into the next contraction.

■ Remember to keep the muscles under the resistance of the weight until you come to the end of your set of repetitions.

How Many?

This will depend on you and your goals. If you want to add roundness by increasing muscle size, then you should work out with somewhat heavier weights and do several sets of 10 to 12 repetitions. The first step will be a warm-up, with lighter weights; the next set will be the heaviest workout; the third should consist of as many repetitions as you can do—perhaps you will be able to do only half the number of the first two sets, or you may be able to do more. This last set should be fairly strenuous.

If your purpose is only to firm up and maintain muscle tone, then you should do one set of as many repetitions as possible until your muscles are tired. The first aim would be to drive your muscles to their limit; the second would be to bring them to a state of tension with the blood circulating throughout so they will be toned and invigorated.

Position

Using weights may cause undue stress on spinal vertebrae and certain ligaments of the body if you do them standing or sitting. You will note that all the exercises in this basic program are designed so that you will be reclining or supported in some way during the workout. We do not recommend that you perform deep-knee bends holding weights of any category. This places too much stress on the spine and the knees.

It is preferable to do weight training in supported positions because this enables you to concentrate the work on the particular muscle groups being exercised at the moment. It takes less energy and prevents the rest of the muscles from becoming fatigued during the workout. It also lessens the chance of hurting yourself through muscle strain, or of rolling over because of lack of balance.

Agility, coordination, and flexibility are best achieved through stretching, yoga, or dance exercises. Weight training is meant to bring your muscles into shape and strength.

How Long Will It Take?

This will depend on the work you put in. Results will not happen in a week. But you should see improvements during the early weeks.

Women who have a background of sports activity will be able to shape up more quickly than those who have never involved themselves in such things. Muscles become conditioned to exercise during the growing years; if you were very active when you were a girl, your muscles will "remember" the early conditioning and respond in a short time. If not, you will have to teach your muscles what exercise is all about.

You should begin to notice changes within the first six weeks, and they should become more pronounced as you continue with your program. If you do not maintain regular discipline and work out two or three times a week, you cannot ever expect to see results. Going to a gym is not like going to Elizabeth Arden. You will not come out the first day looking like a new woman. But the overall results will last a lot longer than the cosmetics that worked their magic at the beauty spa.

What Not to Expect

If you want to lose fat from any part of the body, you should be aware that exercise alone probably will not achieve that for you. It will help because you will be using up stored energy during your workouts, but a change in eating patterns must accompany any weight-loss program. If you are overweight, presumably you got that way by eating too much of the wrong foods. If you stay on the same diet that made you fat, exercise will only bring about shapely muscles beneath the layer of avoirdupois.

Exercise Classes

One would be hard put to find a women's health club that does not have a schedule of supervised exercise classes. In all likelihood, these classes are very much worth your while in addition to your regular gym work. They are designed to provide the kind of stretching and calisthenics that work well to keep a woman's body in healthy shape. Weight training does not offer the kind of stretching and elongation required for overall fitness. Exercise classes are based primarily on the concept of stretching for health. If your gym does not offer such classes, we are including a chapter with some basic stretches to keep you limber and flexible. You can do them either before or after your gym workout. Together, the two types of exercise should provide a complete muscle-fitness program.

What Not to Wear

The favored women's gym costume consists of leotards and dance tights. These items are particularly good because they allow you full mobility through any kind of exercise. They fit like a second skin, so you can see how your muscles work during a given exercise. They also protect the skin from scratches, friction burns, or calluses from using the machines, and against chills during the heat of the exercise.

You should avoid suits that do not let your body expel excess heat. Do not work out in plastic suits that hold body heat in. You may overheat yourself and become excessively fatigued. Your body needs air to evaporate the perspiration and keep its temperature at safe levels during the workout.

The Exercises

Always start by exercising the large muscles of the body first, then move on to the smaller muscles. The buttocks are the largest muscles of the body and should be worked first. In all weight programs except the Nautilus, it is impossible to work just the buttocks without including the thighs.

So we are starting off with three sets of leg exercises. If you are going to be doing exercises with very light weights, then you can do all of the exercises here. If you are actually doing body building, you might want to eliminate the leg exercises in Part Three. Do more intense work, therefore, with Part One.

Leg Exercises—Part 1: Leg Extensions: for front of thighs

■ Sit on edge of the machine and hook ankles behind the padded bar toward the floor.

■ Grasp the edges of the table with your hands and keep your back fairly straight. Be sure you are comfortably braced with hands.

■ Lift legs straight out in front of you, pushing the bar as the legs rise. Lower and raise legs continuously until you have completed all repetitions.

■ Keep the weight resistance on your legs continuously throughout the repetitions; try not to disengage the weights until the end of the exercise.

Leg Curls: for backs of thighs and buttocks

■ Lie face-down on the table with the backs of heels against the upper bar on the machine.

■ Grasp edges of the table with hands for stability.

■ Engage weights and bring your heels toward your derrière. (Allow your hips to rise naturally to accommodate movement.)

■ Continue the movement up and down until the repetitions are completed.

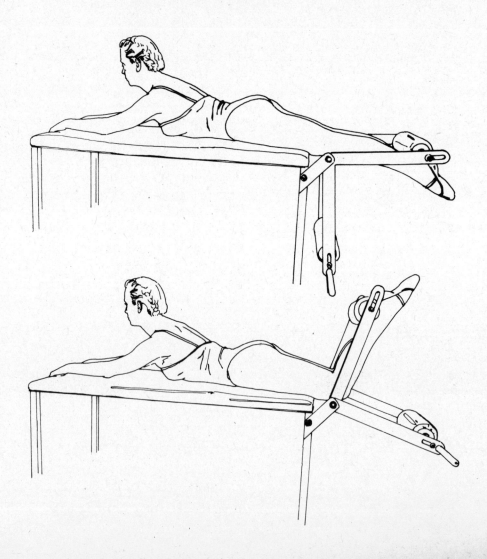

Leg Scissors:

Extremely effective for shaping hips, firming the buttocks, and making the area tighter. Also tones entire leg and gets that soft area of the inner thigh in shape. Do *not* use heavy weights for any of these exercises. If you are working at home, you can do them without weights and get fast results, but you will do many more repetitions. If you are using a weighted pulley machine, run through all exercises with one leg, then change ankles and repeat with the other leg.

First Position:

Lie on back, with head toward the weight stack.

■ Keep legs straight, arms either at sides or under buttocks.

■ Raise weighted leg up as far as possible, keeping it straight, then bring it straight down to floor.

■ Repeat up-and-down movement, with weight resistance kept on the leg through all reps.

Second position:
Lie on side, with weighted leg on top of the other.

■ Have one arm lying out along floor and brace your torso with the other hand on floor.

■ Raise and lower weighted leg, like a scissors. Keep back straight and try not to lift hips off floor during exercise.

Third Position:
Lie on stomach, flat out.

■ You can place hands under face for comfort, or raise head.

■ Raise and lower weighted leg, keeping it as straight as possible. Leave other leg resting as flat as possible on the floor.

Note: Be sure to keep hips aligned on all three positions.

Inverted Leg Press:
for all muscles of the hips, buttocks, and upper legs. If you are active in other sports, or go hiking or climbing, this is a good strengthener for the lower body. It is performed with a machine in which you either sit or lie on your back. Your gym will most likely have the sit-down machine.

■ Press feet against the bar or platform connected to the weights.

■ Extend legs as far as possible, exhaling.

■ Pause.

■ Bring knees to chest, inhaling.

■ Try to keep feet aligned or angled, with toes slightly in toward each other.

Toe Lifts:

for calves and ankle strengthening

- Extend legs all the way and keep them there.

- Push platform away by pointing with the toes.

- Repeat movement for a full set of reps.

Note: If you can't do this on your machine, do calf raises standing up, raising and lowering on toes, with a weighted bar held across the shoulders.

Many women will prefer not to do weighted calf exercises, since this area tends to show muscle definition rather easily. If you want the strength for sports, however, that's how it's done.

Please note that the exercises in Part 2—the scissor moves—can be done at the same time as Part 1 or Part 3 exercises. Do *not* do Part 1 on the same days you do Part 3, since they work the same muscles.

The plans should go like this:

Either: ■ Leg Extensions
      ■ Leg Curls
      ■ Leg Scissors
      ■ Toe Lifts
Or: ■ Leg Press
      ■ Leg Scissors
      ■ Toe Lifts

If you are not interested in developing your calves in any way, you can eliminate the toe lifts altogether. But we suggest that you use this exercise periodically—say, once a week—for toning.

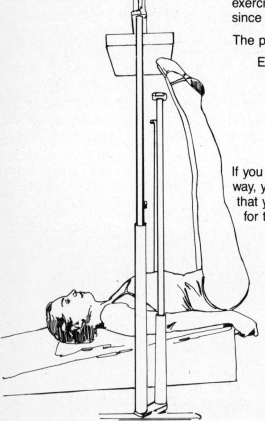

Pulldowns: for upper back, shoulders, latissimus dorsi.

This strengthens the muscles that help make for good posture. It smooths the area over the shoulder blades, helps tone neck and shoulders, and is performed with a weighted pulley.

■ Hold bar behind neck and move away from the machine to engage weights. Kneel, keeping back straight and legs braced apart.

■ Let arms extend fully overhead, inhaling.

■ Pull bar down to your shoulders, keeping elbows wide, exhaling.

■ Pause. Extend arms again.

Keep control of the bar on upward and downward moves. Keep reps and sets at a minimum unless you are working to build up these muscles for swimming or climbing.

Bench Press: for pectorals (chest muscles under the breasts)

Many women never consider doing these exercises. They strengthen the muscles that support the breasts, provide better tone in that area as well as better support, and impart a more youthful line to the bust.

This is performed on a bench, using either a barbell or a bench-press machine. We prefer the machine since it permits better control of the weights.

■ Lie on back with feet up on bench (preferred) or flat on the floor. Do not arch back during this exercise.

■ Push weight straight up from your chest, keeping elbows wide, exhaling.

■ Pause.

■ Lower weights to chest, inhaling.

Do not do this exercise quickly. Take two seconds to raise weights; one second to pause; three to four seconds to lower them. This exercise is to increase strength.

The reason it is preferred to have the feet up on the bench is to keep the spine straight and protect the back from strain. Also, remember to face upward, not turn to the side, during this bench-press exercise.

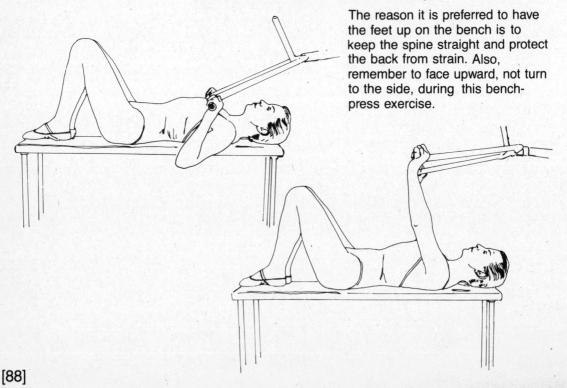

Dumbbell Press:

If you don't like the bench press, this is an alternative. Do it on an incline board.

- Support your whole body on the incline board as shown, holding a dumbbell in each hand.

- Keep dumbbells at chest level, elbows wide.

- Extend arms straight out from chest and touch dumbbells together in midair, exhaling.

- Pause.

- Return dumbbells to chest, inhaling.

These presses can be performed more quickly than the bench press. Remember the importance of keeping elbows wide throughout.

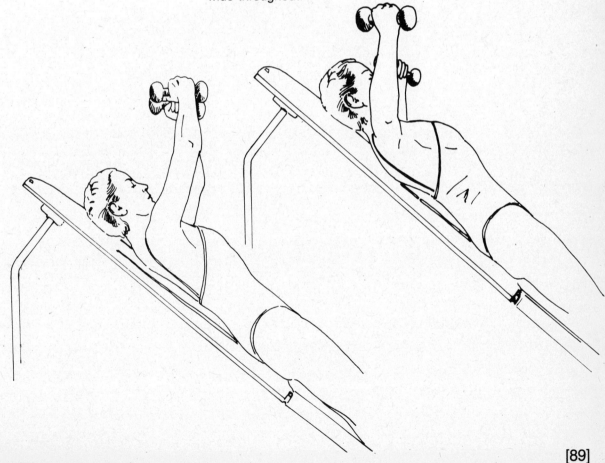

French Curls: for the triceps (backs of arms)

This is important for women. When left to go flabby, this part of the arm becomes a sort of middle-age "wattle." This exercise firms it up.

- Hold one dumbbell in one hand, behind neck, as shown.

- Raise dumbbell, extending arm straight up, exhaling. Keep elbow stationary by stabilizing it with other hand.

- Pause.

- Lower weight again to back of neck, inhaling.

- When reps are completed, repeat with other arm.

Don't use heavy weights here, as they are difficult to control and will increase arm size. You can perform the French curl more slowly for better control, and still increase tone. Don't rush this one.

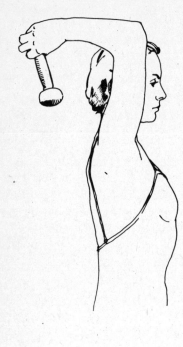

Pressdowns:

alternative to French curl, and you may prefer it. Both arms are exercised at the same time. Use a weighted pulley, the same one you used for pulldowns.

■ Stand with both hands close together, grasping the middle of the bar, with the wire between your hands. Keep feet apart for stability. Stand far enough away from machine to engage weights; keep them engaged throughout.

■ Start with arms extended straight down. Exhale.

■ Bring hands up to chest, close in to body, raising elbows wide. Inhale. *Keep back straight.*

■ Pause.

■ Push bar straight down again. Go immediately into next repetition.

Perform this one slowly for better control. It is a very effective exercise for toning the triceps. Heavier weights will increase strength for sports.

Bicep Curls:

for fronts of arms

Another exercise women tend to ignore. Use light weights for this one, unless you need extra strength in arms for sports or lifting. It is possible to build the bicep shape into a look that we think of as masculine, but male and female arms are identical, so don't worry about it. The only time it will look that way is if you "make a muscle." In a normal relaxed position, it won't bulge. Use an unloaded barbell or two light dumbbells at first, until you know your strength capability.

- Stand holding weight with arm fully extended downward, wide apart on barbell. Hands must come straight up from hip.

- Raise weight up to chest in a smooth movement, exhaling. Keep elbows stationary at sides, or placed on a stand made for this exercise.

- Pause.

- Return arms to full extended position, inhaling.

- Go immediately into next repetition.

Note: These exercises are effective for toning the arms. Women who do not want a bulky look should include an equal number of stretching exercises to keep the arms smooth-looking.

Tummy Tighteners: three different ways to do it

Twists:

This is the fastest way to flatten the tummy, but it is also rather difficult to perform correctly at first. The hips must be stabilized, not moving with the torso. The twists should not be done too fast, but with controlled, steady movements so you don't cramp your back muscles.

- Sit on floor, with legs out in front of you; or sit on a stool, with feet apart to stabilize body. Keep back straight; do not bow out behind or stoop your shoulders.

- Place a bar across your shoulders (or a wooden rod, such as a broomstick) and rest hands extended on it. Or simply keep arms extended straight out.

- Think of arms as pointing east–west.

- Turn upper body to right, bringing arms as much north–south as you can. Exhale. Pause.

- Return to east–west and inhale.

- Repeat twist on the left side.

Start out with 10 to 15 repetitions on each side.

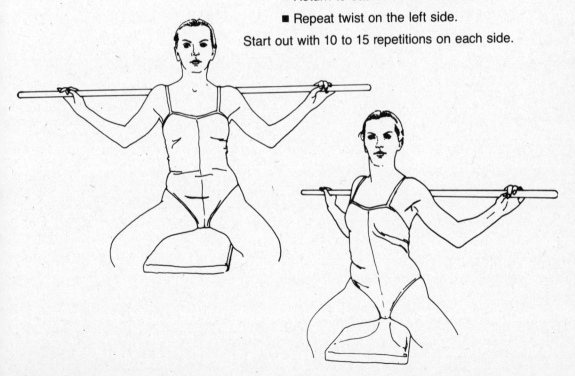

Sit-ups:

Use sit-up board, or anchor feet and keep knees bent.

- Place hands lightly at neck. Lie back, spine straight.

- Curl yourself up, using abdominal muscles to bring your chin to your knees. Exhale as you rise.

- Pause.

- Lower yourself to almost a full flat-out position, inhaling, and go immediately into next rep.

You can also do these going only as far up as you need to bring the abdominals into contraction.

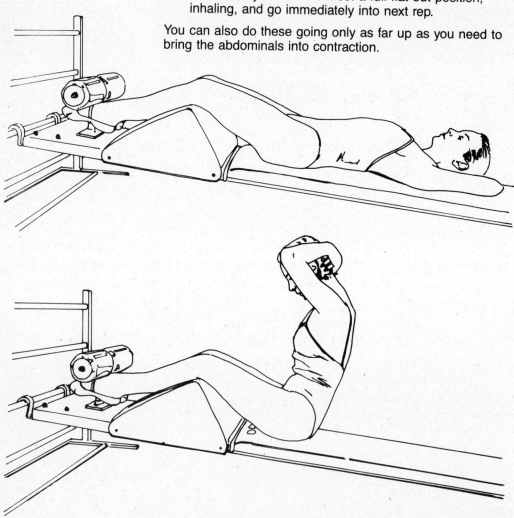

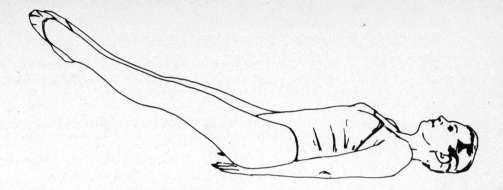

Leg Raises:

Many women prefer these to sit-ups. Be careful not to strain lower back when lifting legs.

- Lie flat out on floor. Place hands, palms down, under buttocks. Keep feet together and body aligned.

- Concentrate on abdominals. Inhale. Use abdominals to raise your legs straight up from floor. Do not bend knees.

- Exhale as you raise legs.

A variation of this would be to use a flat sit-up board, holding on to the foot anchor with your hands and bringing legs straight up and down, or bringing knees into chest.

Exercise for Lower Back:

You should exercise the lower back equally with the abdominals, according to many exercise experts. It may be that the leg and hip exercises provide adequate strengthening for this area, but stretching and strengthening exercises are important. This "cobra" exercise is favored for strengthening the lumbar region. Use smooth, controlled movements to avoid cramps and pinched nerves. Do not overdo this exercise. A series of 10 repetitions is a pretty strong workout.

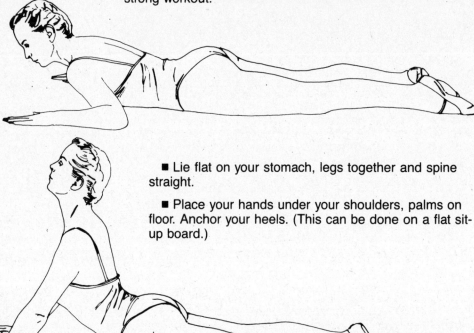

■ Lie flat on your stomach, legs together and spine straight.

■ Place your hands under your shoulders, palms on floor. Anchor your heels. (This can be done on a flat sit-up board.)

■ Gently raise head and let your torso follow smoothly.

■ Keep hands on floor as stabilizers, not to push yourself up. Exhale as you rise.

■ Pause at "top" of rise.

■ Return to flat-down position, inhaling.

If you prefer a fuller stretching of abdomen, you can inhale on the way up instead.

Keeping It Up

Staying in shape is as important as *getting* in shape. Do not think of it as a one-shot deal. Do not stop exercising once you've reached your goal. You can, at that point, limit your time at the gym, but you cannot eliminate it, or you'll return to the realm of the softies. The months of intense concentration and effort should be followed by weekly maintenance visits to the gym. You can go twice a week and do one easy and one intense workout each week. Or you can go three times a week and do basic run-throughs, with periodic intense workouts every six visits. By that time you should be in tune with your body enough to know how it will react to exercise and layoffs. Part of the learning process is getting to know how to gauge your own needs.

Attitude is important. You must do the exercise—the exercise cannot work you. Do not take a passive approach. Concentrate on what you are doing. Give the time at the gym its due. Learn how your body responds. Working with light weights, you may find it easy to let your mind wander. Gain control of your thoughts as well as of your muscles during this time.

Count your repetitions while you do them. Keep your mind on controlling the weights and making sure that you are providing enough resistance on your muscles so that they do enough work to achieve the results you want. If, for example, you are doing the leg scissors, you may just keep pumping away without counting and end up not knowing how many reps you did.

You must also maintain an awareness of your growth. You may find that the weights are becoming lighter and lighter. At a certain point you may want to increase them if you are going for more strength, or increase them periodically to maintain your tone. Working with weights that are too light will not build any muscle; if the weights are very light, and you are used to them on a regular basis, you will need some extra resistance at times to keep your tone at a high level.

It is also extremely important to stay with the plan you've set and build on it. Erratic patterns will never bring you a good body. You must do the required number of repetitions each time; you should not suddenly do a burst of 100 reps one day because you feel superenergetic. If you have that much strength, then increase the workout reps and resistance overall to give yourself a meaningful workout each visit to the gym.

Set the discipline and keep it going. The psychological effect of the scientific approach is important here. Your mind tells your body what to do. If your mind is approaching the workouts erratically, the body will not be able to respond. Hook up the mind and the body. Devote your time at the gym *only* to the workout. Do not bring a book to read during the scissors kicks. Leave the outside world outside for the time you're there. That's the only way to shape up.

NAUTILUS

Nautilus is a name that has suddenly become a very hot item along the health-club circuit. These fascinating weight-lifting machines are wrapped in a sort of glamour and magic, since they seem to be the perfect answer for people who want to shape up but don't really want to spend a lot of time at it. Indeed, you can redesign your body in about a third of the time needed with conventional weights and equipment, and with much less time spent at the gym on any given day. Because the principles and use of the Nautilus are significantly different from those of traditional weight-lifting apparatus, we are devoting a special chapter to these machines.

Nautilus weight-lifting machines were developed in Deland, Florida, by Arthur Jones, owner of Nautilus Sports/Medical Industries—the company that manufactures them. The first machines were introduced around 1969 and presented a whole new approach to fitness, muscle building, and shaping up at all levels. Nautilus machines provide strength training for athletes, medical therapy, or basic shaping-up for the "average" man, woman, or teenager.

There are Nautilus machines to exercise each muscle group in the body. Some gyms carry a full set so that members can develop the entire body without utilizing any other equipment. Many gyms and health clubs have at least one or two machines. It should be noted that they are made to be used on the basis of the Nautilus method of exercise and will not give you satisfactory results if you try to use them like free weights, as you will see during the course of this chapter.

The key to Nautilus is in its cam—an adjusting wheel shaped like a nautilus seashell. It corresponds to the structure of the muscles in the body and is designed to provide maximum concentration of stress on the muscles being exercised. The cam enables you to isolate muscle groups and use them at their maximum ability during each exercise of the workout.

Because of this "maximizing" aspect, you need to perform one set of 8 to 12 repetitions for each upper-body muscle group and 15 to 20 reps for lower-body groups. A full body workout on Nautilus machines takes less than 30 minutes. No other exercise is required to shape up the entire body. Nautilus claims that its machines provide 90 percent efficiency during a workout and that free weights can provide only 10 percent.

The company recommends that *only one* set of repetitions be done each workout session, since the cam lets you receive more effective work in one set than you would get by using free weights for several sets.

The Cam

The cam is shaped only incidentally like a seashell. As stated above, it actually corresponds to the construction of your muscles, which are stronger in the middle and weaker at either end. The cam adjusts the weight stress on the muscle as you work the machine, so the heaviest load comes at the strongest part of the muscle and is lessened at the weakest points. The cam also provides a high concentration of work for the muscles, since the machine holds you in a position so that only the muscles meant to be exercised do the work. When using free weights, you have a tendency to "cheat" or help by jerking the weights through the positive part of the movement with the rest of the body. This is eliminated more easily on the Nautilus machines. Only the muscles meant to be worked on each machine are exercised.

The result: You can do much less in the way of repetitions and in less time and obtain faster muscle development. The construction of the Nautilus machines also makes them appropriate for use by women who want to tone their muscles without losing their feminine form, by men who need gym work but don't have a lot of time to devote to it, and by pre-adults who want to start on a program that may or may not lead to pro-athlete or bodybuilder status.

It should be noted that the standard Nautilus program tends to develop a "nice" natural build along your own genetic lines. This is because the body's natural needs were allowed to dictate the design of the machines. Although bodybuilder muscles are spectacular, it should be remembered that they are, in fact, muscles held in an unnatural size through force. They are not unhealthy, but they can exist only at that supersize through extreme effort on a concentrated basis.

Nautilus can be used to achieve and/or maintain competition-size muscularity, but the basic program we are describing here is for beginners.

Momentary Muscle Failure

The reason why Nautilus can provide full exercise benefits in brief workouts of less than 30 minutes is due to something called "momentary muscle failure." In the use of free weights, you may never actually arrive at this point. On Nautilus you *must* get to this point with each muscle group in every workout; otherwise you may wonder why the results promised don't happen.

Momentary muscle failure means exactly what it sounds like. You reach the point where you are unable to perform the exercise *in proper form* one more time. Your muscles just won't do it again. This is based on the premise that you have done all the previous repetitions in correct form nonstop. If you pause for a few seconds, releasing the weights from the muscles, you will, of course, be able to continue and perform more reps. The muscle failure is, as we said, momentary.

This stopping point, caused by total fatigue of the muscle, is your indication that you have done your workout properly and can move on to the next machine or to the showers, in full knowledge that your muscles will now do the rest. It's important when using Nautilus to remember that you should not rest and do more reps or another set. This would be overworking and only serves to break down the muscle cells more than they can be replaced in a reasonable length of time. Constant overworking will have the totally negative effect of tearing down the muscle tissue, not building it up at all.

When working with Nautilus, always remember that the point of momentary muscle failure is your cutoff point for the exercise for that day.

Proper Form

The proper movement while on a Nautilus machine is characterized by smooth, controlled motions. This should also be your form for free weights, but on Nautilus it is easier to achieve because you are stabilized in a position that makes it possible to isolate the muscles being worked.

Here again, you divide the single repetition into positive and negative movements, the positive being the contraction of the muscle, the negative being the elongation that follows as you return the weight to its starting point.

The positive movement should take about two seconds to perform completely. The muscle is held in contraction for another second; then four seconds are allowed for the negative movement. A set of 10 repetitions on the Nautilus would take about one minute to complete.

This counting of seconds as you exercise will provide discipline and control. It will also take your mind off any negative thoughts, such as building a mental resistance against the increasing stress of the weights. Become one with the machine, letting it coordinate with the movements of your body. This smoothness and control will greatly enhance the success of your program.

Although the Nautilus machines are designed to place you in the correct position for each exercise, they are not foolproof. It is definitely possible to use Nautilus incorrectly. Bodybuilders often try to do "jerks" and heaves with these machines, as well as burnouts—more and more sets of reps until the muscle is totally exhausted. Such actions will lead to negative effects.

It is also possible to be seated incorrectly on a Nautilus. If you are at a gym where full instruction is part of the policy, have the instructor set the seat position for you. If you're on your own, adjust the seat so that the cam pivot is aligned with the working joint of your body. (See illustration.)

Correct form also means eliminating body English, facial grimaces, and the use of other parts of the body to help you perform the exercise. Isolation of muscle groupings is an essential part of success on these machines. Even "making faces" cuts the efficiency of the workout by taking energy and concentration away from the muscles being exercised. Remember, lifting weights is not meant to be an ego trip; there is no need to impress anyone that you can go one more rep at all costs. If you are unable to perform at least eight repetitions of any exercise on Nautilus, this only means you are set at a weight that is too heavy for your present development.

The 8-to-12 Routine

Nautilus machines are designed to be used when doing one set of 8 to 12 repetitions on each machine. This "repetition range" allows you to have a guideline for moving up to the next weight. The first time you work out, you are expected to reach momentary muscle failure within the 8-to-12 range of repetitions. When you have developed your strength to the point where the 12-rep limit no longer causes momentary muscle failure, you should increase the weight and lower the reps to eight again, or within the repetition range. This pattern continues throughout the program.

Prestretching

Prestretching is a term you'll hear if you hang around a Nautilus gym for any length of time. Prestretching is *not* the same as stretching, nor is it done for the same purpose. Prestretching is a technique used by athletes to obtain more muscle power to perform a sports task. For instance, a baseball pitcher will prestretch his arm muscles by backing up a little just before throwing the ball. This brings more muscle fibers into play and provides him with extra strength that puts more power behind the ball.

When used in the Nautilus workout, prestretching will let you obtain more efficiency to perform the movements correctly and with more power; over the long run it can enhance muscle development because it brings more muscle fibers into action. The technique works like this:

As you are lowering the weight during the negative part of the repetition, you come to the point where you would go immediately into the positive contraction again. Normally you would not release the weight but would go down only to a certain point, keeping the weight on your muscles. To do the prestretch you would ease up, slightly releasing the tension on your muscles with a little faster movement just before going into the positive movement of the next repetition. In short, you are letting go of the weight merely enough to bring more muscle fibers into play and therefore are increasing your strength. Ultimately, your body will respond by developing these extra muscle fibers as well, and greater strength and size will result.

WHAT TO WEAR ON THE NAUTILUS

Although there is no rule for this, the most practical clothing to wear when using Nautilus machines is that which covers the greatest area. Sweat pants and T-shirts with short sleeves are the most practical. The reason? Since on any given Nautilus machine you are either sitting or lying on something that supports your whole body, you will be perspiring profusely. It is not very pleasant to sit in a pool of someone else's sweat when it's your turn at the machine, nor will others relish sitting in your puddle, either.

Prestretching is not necessary to your program, but it can be useful. The technique is primarily of interest to people such as football players who want to develop strength for sports activities, or to bodybuilders who want to increase their muscle size. If you do choose to use it, ask someone who is familiar with the technique to demonstrate it first. A little practice is needed to get it right. Prestretching isn't necessary on every repetition, but it may be helpful if you are having a tired day and require an extra lift toward the end of your set. You can incorporate it on alternate repetitions, or you can leave it out altogether. Prestretching can also be an asset later on in your program, when you may feel you want an added boost or want to refine your workouts. Most people will find, however, that the usual technique without prestretching will be all they'll ever need.

Negative Resistance

As you work out with Nautilus you will hear people talking a lot about "negatives." These machines are constructed so that you can do increased work by performing only the second, or negative, part of the repetition. Some machines require that someone else move the machine through the positive movement so you can resist against the negative movement. You can carry out many more negative movements than positive, since you are not "lifting" the weight but simply letting it down to the ground. This is the reason why competition power lifters are judged only by how much they can lift—not by how much they can put down. Extra negative movements allow you to achieve a higher-intensity workout by making more demands on your muscular ability. It is not necessary to do extra negatives to see results in development, but if you are already in good shape and want to advance faster, doing them can enhance your progress.

Many of the sit-down Nautilus machines are equipped with foot pedals, so you can push the weights into midposition and perform just the negative resistance movement with upper-body or arm muscles. When moving the machine through the positive movement, remember to help with the muscle being "negatived"; don't simply rest through this part.

Again, negative exercises are special techniques designed to punch up your strength. During the early stages of your program it is better to stay with the standard movements until your body is conditioned to the point where refinements can be done properly.

Review of Correct Form

■ Use only the muscle groups to be worked on each machine. Do not help with other parts of the body.

■ Take two seconds for the positive move; pause one second; take four counts for the negative. Allow no time to lapse before starting the next repetition.

■ Stop when you reach momentary muscle failure.

■ Go on to the next machine.

The Program

As with free weights, Nautilus works the large muscles first. There is actually a scientific explanation for this. Essentially, the principle is that it is not possible to bring the larger muscles to momentary muscle failure if you work the smaller muscles to exhaustion first. The balance of the muscular system makes it necessary to work from large to small. This does not, as you will see, mean from bottom to top. The largest muscles in the body are the gluteals—or the buttocks. The Nautilus sytem works these and the lower back first. (This is good from another point of view, since it is the best machine for demonstrating clearly how the cam must be aligned with the moving joint. In this case the cam is aligned with the hip socket. Since the cam is totally visible, and since a strap holds you in position, you can use the Nautilus as an example of exactly how the whole concept works.)

Note: In this chapter we are discussing only the machines that are likely to be found in most health clubs. There are other Nautilus machines that exercise the neck and different parts of the body, but these are usually used in gyms for athletes rather than in the average health spa.

How Much Weight?

Hopefully, a knowledgeable instructor will be on hand the first time to help you determine the proper seat positions and starting weight for your size and strength. If you are on your own, you will find that Nautilus weight stacks are labeled on a "1-2-3" basis, rather than telling you how much each plate weighs. The pound weight of each plate in the stack is 10 pounds.

A Nautilus spokesman suggests that the "S.W.A.G." method be used to determine how much weight you will start with. S.W.A.G. means "Scientific Wild-Assed Guessing." Or, you pick a weight number that you are fairly sure you can handle and lock the key into it. If you can perform less than these minimum reps for that machine, lower the weight by an appropriate amount.

The weight is too light if you can perform more than the maximum number of reps in the repetition ranges. But you will know immediately if a weight is too light for you; it will fairly fly out of your hands.

Proper weight resistance lets you work with some stress at the start and becomes progressively more and more difficult as you approach the maximum number of reps. You should have to work through the whole set.

Remember the importance of momentary muscle failure even this first time. If on your second or third visits you are not achieving it in the repetition range, increase the weight to a level that is enough to get you there. *Working with weights that are too light for your strength will prevent you from developing your muscles at all.*

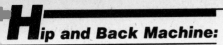ip and Back Machine:

for buttocks and lower back

1. Lie on back with both legs over roller pads.

2. Align hip joints with the axis of each cam.

3. Fasten belt, not too tightly, leaving about 3 inches of play. Grasp handles lightly.

4. Extend both legs fully, feet down toward floor, letting back arch. Push handles with hands to stabilize yourself.

5. Allow one leg to bend back up toward chest as high as it will go, keeping other leg fully extended. Stretch legs as far apart as possible.

6. Extend the bent leg forward again; hold both legs straight out at full extension, toes pointed. Arch lower back and contract buttocks muscles. (THIS POINT COMPLETES THE POSITIVE MOVEMENT OF THE EXERCISE.)

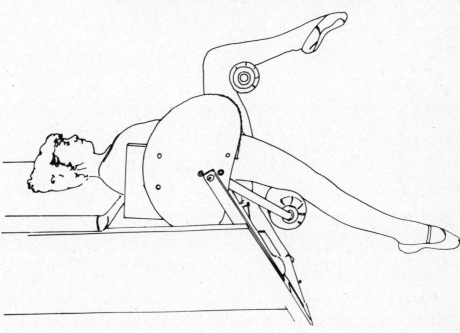

7. Repeat procedure with the other leg.

Note 1: Keep the movements flowing. Count two seconds as you push the bent leg into full extension. Pause for one second at the buttocks contraction. Allow a count of 3 or 4 to bring the leg into the best position.

Note 2: Many instructors will tell you that this is only a warm-up exercise. In fact, it is an essential exercise, and will help you maintain the overall strength balance of the muscular system.

Note 3: Some people will tell you that you should not work with heavy weights on this machine. The same principle of momentary muscle failure applies here, but with one exception. If you are already very strong in the hips and legs and want to concentrate on the upper body, don't move up progressively on this machine. Instead, do a maintenance program to stay at the same weight, or eliminate this exercise periodically from the routine. If you are "maintaining," it is not necessary to reach momentary muscle failure on every workout; you can stop short of muscle failure, say, twice a week, or do one intense and two very light workouts per week. This is where your own judgment comes into play.

Leg Extension:

quadriceps (frontal thighs)

1. Sit on machine with ankles behind roller pads, knees snug against the seat.

2. Keep head and shoulders against seat back throughout exercise.

3. Extend legs smoothly out in front of you, lifting the roller pad to its full extension. (This is the POSITIVE MOVEMENT.)

4. Pause.

5. Lower legs to original position (NEGATIVE MOVEMENT). Go immediately into next rep.

> *Note:* To do only negatives with this machine, use both legs to raise roller pads and one leg to perform the negative movement.

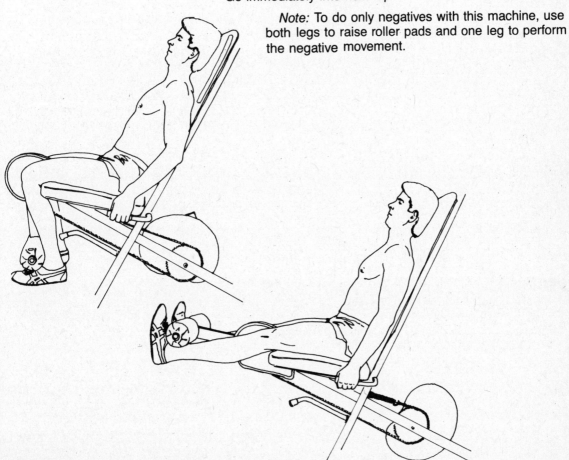

Leg-Press Machine:

quadriceps, hamstrings, and buttocks. (This machine is part of the leg-extension apparatus from the previous exercise. Some gyms do not have it.)

1. Remain in seated position. Place both feet on the foot pads, with toes pointed slightly inward.

2. Straighten both legs to engage the weights (POSITIVE MOVEMENT).

3. Return to bent-leg position and immediately go into next rep.

Note: On both these exercises you may have to do some seat or back-rest positioning. Also, avoid gripping handles too tightly or tensing the neck and upper body—or the face—to "urge" yourself through the exercises.

Leg-Curl Machine:

1. Lie face-down on machine.

2. Place feet under roller pads, with kneecaps just over the edge of the bench.

3. Lightly grasp handles under bench to stabilize your body. There is a tendency to slip around on this machine.

4. Bring feet up and try to touch your heels to the buttocks. You may not actually get there, but go as far as possible. Lift butt to accommodate the movement (POSITIVE MOVEMENT).

5. Pause at point of full muscle contraction.

6. Slowly lower legs to original position (NEGATIVE MOVEMENT).

Note 1: Toes should not be pointed during this exercise. If possible, keep them in position, with toes flexed toward front of knee.

Note 2: Some instructors will tell you to keep your butt down. The proper movement is as indicated above.

[111]

Pullover Machine:

latissimus dorsi muscles and torso (back). Shoulder joints should be aligned with axis of each cam. Fasten seat belt *tightly* around hips. Keep back and head straight against the seat back.

1. Use feet to press foot bar to bring elbow pads into position at chin level. Place elbows on pads and release foot bar.

2. Keep hands open and resting, not pushing on curved bar.

3. Bring elbows up and over, stretching back as far as you can. Allow rib cage to rise naturally.

4. Pushing with elbows, bring hand bar all the way down to touch your stomach. (This is POSITIVE MOVEMENT.)

5. Pause.

6. Slowly return to stretched-back position behind head (NEGATIVE) and immediately do next rep.

Note 1: Look straight ahead during movement. Do not move head or torso out of position.

Note 2: Before the first repetition on this machine, it's best to keep your feet controlling the weights and bring your arms all the way back over the head to determine how much weight they can handle in this stretched-out position. Serious imbalances of right-to-left muscle strength can cause cramps, and misalignment of vertebrae if you are working past your strength. Be careful.

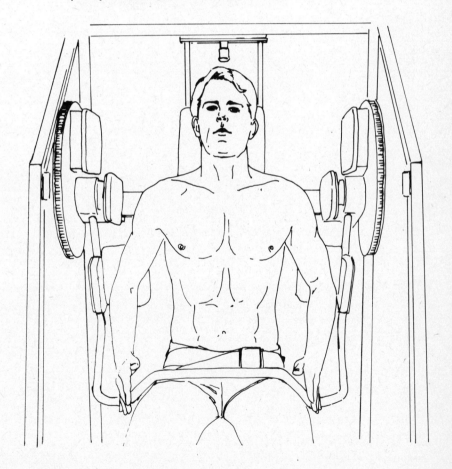

Behind-Neck Machine:

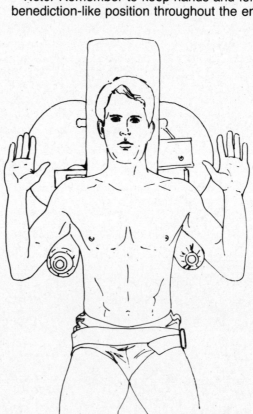

latissimus dorsi (muscles)

1. Adjust seat so that shoulder joints are aligned with cams.

2. Fasten seat belt snugly. Keep knees together.

3. Place triceps (backs of arms) between padded rollers above your head. Cross forearms behind neck.

4. Bring both arms downward until upper arms are horizontal to body (POSITIVE MOVEMENT). Hands should be held in position shown in illustration.

5. After a pause, slowly return to crossed-arms position over head (NEGATIVE MOVEMENT). Repeat next rep immediately.

Note: Remember to keep hands and forearms in this benediction-like position throughout the entire exercise.

Double Chest Machine: pectoral muscles of chest and deltoids (shoulders)

Part 1:
Adjust seat so that shoulders will be directly underneath axes of cams when elbows are held together in front of chest. Adjust weights for this first part. Weights will be different, in most cases, for the second part of this machine. Seat belt is fastened snugly.

1. Place one forearm, then the other, behind the movement pads. This will engage the weight stack, and resistance will be on the muscles until you remove your forearms from pads.

2. Lightly grasp handles, with thumbs around the knob. Keep head against seat back.

3. Push with forearms (not hands) and try to touch elbows together in front of chest (POSITIVE MOVEMENT).

4. Return arms to wide-out position (NEGATIVE MOVEMENT). Go immediately into next repetition. Remove arms after last rep and immediately start next exercise.

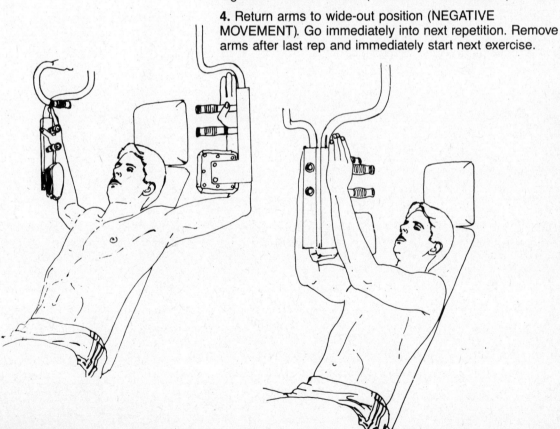

Part 2:
decline press for chest, shoulders, and triceps

1. Reset weights if necessary.

2. Use foot pedal to bring side handles into position and engage weight stack. Grasp handles with parallel grip.

3. Keep head back, torso erect. Don't arch the back.

4. Press bars forward (POSITIVE MOVEMENT).

5. Pause.

6. Keeping elbows wide and horizontal, do NEGATIVE MOVEMENT, bringing arms back to point of full extension. Go immediately into next rep.

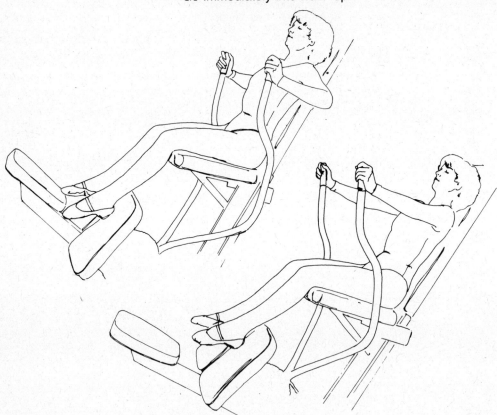

Double Shoulder Machine:

Part 1:

lateral raise for deltoids

1. Adjust seat so that shoulder joints are aligned with cams. Fasten seat belt snugly. Grasp handles lightly, enabling backs of hands and forearms to press against movement pads. (Keep ankles lightly crossed.)

2. Lead with elbows, keeping wrists locked; raise both arms to horizontal position out from body (POSITIVE MOVEMENT).

3. Pause.

4. Lower resistance for NEGATIVE MOVEMENT. Repeat next rep immediately.

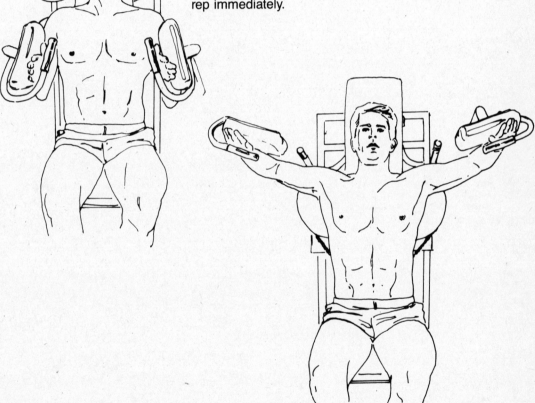

Part 2:

overhead press for deltoids and triceps

1. Readjust weights if necessary.

2. Grasp handles above shoulders. Press straight up for POSITIVE MOVEMENT.

3. Slowly lower weights, keeping elbows wide (NEGATIVE MOVEMENT). Repeat next rep immediately.

Note: Do not arch the back during these exercises. Do not lift legs off seat to help movement.

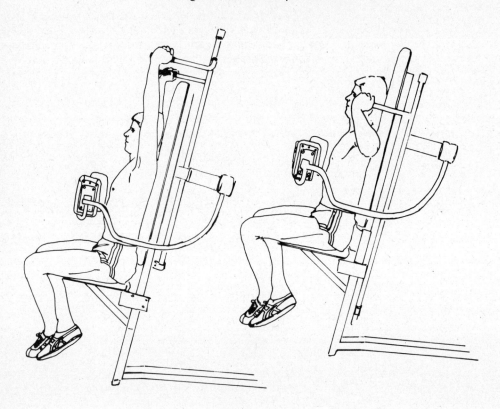

Arm-Curl Machine:

Nautilus makes several models of machines with which to perform curl exercises on the biceps and triceps of the arms. Some of these machines are designed to allow you to exercise one arm at a time, or both arms if you choose. We are not going to discuss each machine, although your health club may stock several of them. They all work on the basic Nautilus principle of aligning the *elbow joints* with the axes of the cams and performing the curls with two seconds for the positive movement, a one-second pause at full contraction, and four seconds for the negative resistance.

As stated, some machines are designed so that one arm is contracted while the other is at full extension; thus, in effect, you are doing the positive movement with the right arm while performing the negative resistance with the left.

Part 1:

biceps. On this machine you must load the weights onto the peg yourself. There is no seat adjustment, but a seat pad may be added for extra height.

1. Place elbows on padded armrest in front of you. Align elbow joint with cam axis.

2. Grasp the curved bar with hands together and palms up.

3. Curl bar smoothly all the way up to your neck (POSITIVE MOVEMENT).

4. Pause.

5. Slowly return bar to stretched position (NEGATIVE MOVEMENT) and repeat next rep immediately.

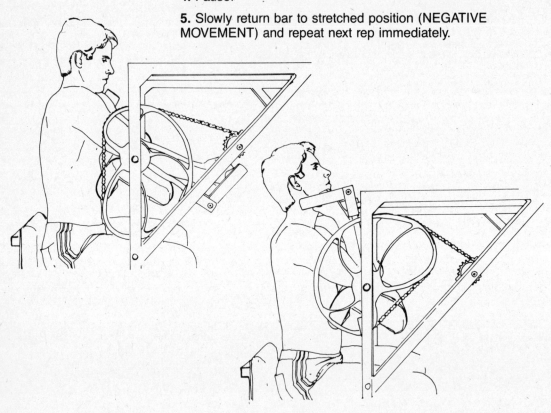

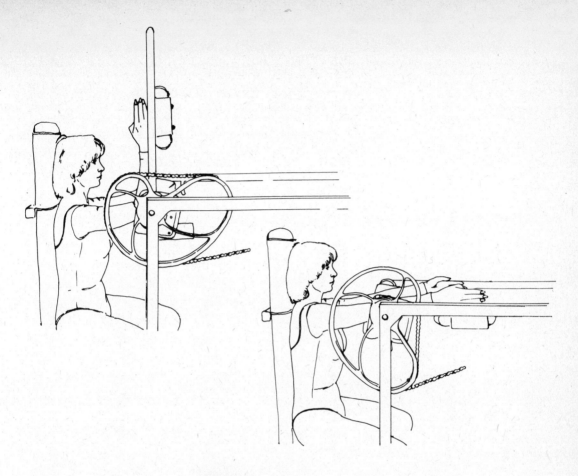

Part 2:

triceps. Sit and align yourself with elbows at the cam axis, as in the first part.

1. Place hands against pads as if making a chopping motion, thumbs up.

2. Keeping wrists straight and elbows firmly on the armrest, smoothly extend your forearm and perform the POSITIVE MOVEMENT until arms are fully extended.

3. Pause.

4. Slowly bring arms back to original position (NEGATIVE MOVEMENT) and immediately repeat next rep.

trapezius and back of neck

Care should be taken with this machine, and it should be used last, since the smallest muscles of the body are worked with it. Do not overload it or painful stiffness will occur in the neck. Feel your way carefully. The machine is based on the shoulder-shrug exercise done with free weights. However, the intensity of a Nautilus workout is perhaps more evident on this machine than on any of the others. Also, there is no aligning of joints with a cam here, since no major joints are used.

1. Seat yourself high enough to keep the weights engaged while remaining erect in the seat.

2. Place forearms between the two pads before you. You will have to bend your back to do this.

3. Keep palms open and facing upward; press backs of hands firmly against bottom pads.

4. Straighten torso to engage weight stack.

5. Smoothly raise or "shrug" shoulders as high as possible. Do not jerk them. Remember the two-second count for this POSITIVE MOVEMENT.

6. Pause.

7. Slowly lower weights for NEGATIVE MOVEMENT. Repeat next rep immediately.

Note: Keep elbows by sides when shrugging. Do not lean back or try to stand. Do not disengage the weights during the movement.

Maintenance with the Nautilus

An almost hypothetical question arises after you study the Nautilus machines for a while. What happens, you ask, when I come to the last weight on the machine and have conquered the maximum reps on it? Where do I go from there? Needless to say, you would be rather large-muscled at that point, and probably will have decided to level off long before then to maintain your body where you want it.

Maintenance on the Nautilus is the same as maintenance with free weights. You level off. You stop working out three days a week. You readjust yourself to fewer days, or to exercising at varying intensities. For example, you could do an intense workout on Wednesdays, a lighter one on Fridays, and a very light one on Mondays. Or you might skip a week.

Maintenance of muscles is accomplished more or less by keeping your eye on them. At times they will start to weaken from lack of exercise. You will work intensely for a while, then slack off so you don't get too big. At that point you will know your body well enough to be able to gauge what to what to where, when to do it, and how often.

Postscript

Remember that when working with Nautilus, you must concentrate on the abdominal muscles last. Nautilus has made a machine for these muscles, called the abductor, but it is not found in all gyms and is no longer being manufactured. Regular stomach exercises are adequate for use in a Nautilus program.

STRETCHING OUT

Superb as weight lifting can make you look, it is only part of an exercise plan for healthy muscles. Stretching is essential for anyone who is interested in more than just the cosmetic aspect of exercise.

Stretching for a week or so prior to beginning a weight-training program will prime your body for the weights. It will certainly give you the extra energy you will need for the new, hard work, as well as the mental boost that is so important.

While weight lifting concentrates blood into the muscles, stretching "opens" you up so that the blood can move more easily, taking out toxins and wastes that can cause blockages, congestion, and, ultimately, health problems. If you maintain a subregimen of stretching exercises in addition to your weight routines, you will experience less soreness and less stiffness, and will be less prone to cramps, strains, and injuries.

Stretching does not interfere with the basic shape that weight training brings about; however, this elongation refines the overall body form, making the muscles look more natural, less "bumpy," more aesthetic. Many pro bodybuilders are instituting stretching routines into their personal regimens to give flexibility and greater agility to those gleaming, Detroit-designed muscles.

Although through the years women's exercise programs have included stretching all along, men have discovered its value only recently. The most immediate benefit from stretching is that it leaves you in a more relaxed state, destroys tension knots, and—though not immediately—it provides greater muscle tone in a very brief time, usually within two weeks.

There is some disagreement about the manner in which stretching should be integrated into a weight-lifting program—or into any type of fitness program. Some experts in sports medicine tend to believe that you should stretch only once a day and that it should be done apart from aerobic or weight workouts. Some bodybuilders do all of their exercises in one time allotment but segment each, performing aerobics, weight training, and stretching in consecutive sequence.

One medical researcher of sports medicine told us that the best way to integrate any program is to allow at least a four-hour break between weight workouts and stretching, and that aerobic exercises should be performed either on alternate days or five hours after the weight workouts. The reason for these breaks is to give the body time to "normalize" before it gets into another kind of stressful activity. The point, simply stated, is that your body primes itself differently to perform each type of exercise, and it is healthier to provide time to switch over between regimens.

This last approach appears to be the most commendable, since it comes out of scientific methods of research, whereas many bodybuilders have set up their personal programs by instinct. The programs work well for them but may not be right for everyone.

Because everybody reacts in a personal way to different types of exercise, it is difficult to offer concrete advice for "everyone" on this matter. The human body is an amazingly adaptable organism, and you may find that doing all your exercises together is the best way for you, psychologically as well as timewise. If you want to exercise every day, you *must* alternate between aerobics and weights, since you definitely should not do the same exercise day after day.

You can do your stretching exercises on a daily basis, but caution should be taken at the start not to overdo it. Stretching is more of a releasing rather than a conditioning, a letting-go rather than a building-up. Because of that unique aspect, it does not appear to have a deleterious effect on your body if performed daily.

Points to Remember

■ You can do a lot of various stretching exercises over a long workout period—say as long as an hour and a half. You can also do a few basic stretches in a few minutes and still achieve a great deal of flexibility.

■ Although it is good to stretch stiff muscles throughout the day as they need it, the best approach is to do your stretching in a disciplined, formal workout. This will condition your body to the program, just as with weight training. However you set up your program, make sure it is "set up."

■ Don't try to "force-stretch" your muscles into any position that they are too short to achieve. Stretch them according to your ability. Some people have inherited shorter muscles genetically, while others are born with the ability to do a cheerleader's split.

■ Don't stretch past the point of pain, but don't keep stretching until it hurts, either. Bring yourself to the point where your muscles *begin* to strain, and let that be your stopping point. With every subsequent workout you will find that you can go a little further. Remember, the doing of it alone is sufficient exercise. It isn't necessary to accomplish more than keeping your muscles limber.

■ It is best to perform stretching exercises on your back. The floor will support you and relieve you of the additional burden of having to balance yourself. This minimizes the possibility of pain or muscle damage.

■ Exhale as you stretch, to get the feeling of opening outward from the center of your body. This will provide a psychological "freeing" that will be reflected physically in your muscles. You'll end up by feeling lighter and more relaxed. Get the sense of exhalation *doing* the stretch for you.

■ *Relax* into the stretch rather than "tensing outward." Imagine yourself extending past your fingers and toes while you do the movements. Stretching should never be pushed. You should have a feeling of increased relaxation as you proceed through the movements.

■ "Feel" what you are doing as you do it. Tune in to the consciousness of the muscles and become aware of how they extend and elongate.

If you are involved in a hatha-yoga program, you already have a more-than-adequate stretching program and need not bother with finding another one. Dancers also have stretching exercises built into their daily lives, although many dancers find that extra stretching and flexibility classes are helpful to them.

It should be noted here that stretching provides you with a lot of energy. These exercises tend to release the energy already stored in your body and bring more oxygen through to your system. The result is an abundance of immediate energy. Lassitude and fatigue are eliminated, and you will find that you need less sleep. This may appear as a problem at first—you will think you have insomnia. But eventually you will adjust to this condition and work it into your patterns of living.

These exercises operate well in conjunction with aerobics because they heighten the performance of the body as a whole and the body responds more efficiently to the movement of the heart. The heart fares better because circulation is improved, and the blood and fluids flow more easily through the system. Stress is reduced, which makes it even easier for the cardiovascular system to perform well.

Because the body is more limber, there is less resistance to movement. You move with less effort, use less energy, and place less wear on the entire body. For these reasons, the body stays stronger for a longer period of time. This may be one explanation of why dancers' bodies appear to be almost indestructible.

Breathing

Breath control is important in all exercises. It is vital to keep oxygen pumping continually into the lungs during workouts of any kind. In weight lifting, the breath helps move the weights and eases the stress of the workout while heading off fatigue. With stretching exercises, oxygenation is almost the whole point. You should breathe deeply and fully, filling your lungs completely. Let your breathing become the focal point of each stretching movement. Regard the physical movement as secondary to the breathing.

Inhale, filling the lungs easily and letting the abdominal muscles relax to accommodate the expanding lungs.

Exhale as you elongate the muscles into the stretch. Think of the escaping breath as a vehicle that takes the muscles out into the stretch. Let the breath exhalation tell you how long to maintain the stretch. Let the last part of each breath escape by itself.

The exhalation should always be longer than the inhalation —about half again as long as it took you to inhale.

For the back:

There are two ways to do this same exercise: reclining on a bench or a bed, or supporting yourself on your feet. It is preferred that beginners use the reclining position since there is no support under the thighs during the standing position.

First:
reclining

- Align your spine on the bench or bed, with legs slanting from the hip to the floor.

- Bring one knee all the way up to the chest and use hands to get a good stretch. Leave the other leg in its slanted position.

- Return leg to floor. Repeat movement with other leg.

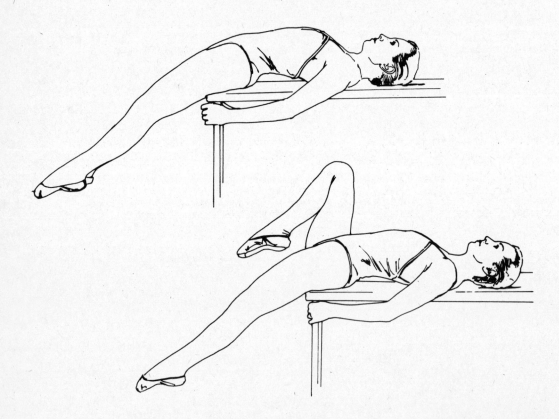

Second:
standing

- Place one leg out behind you, bringing chest down to the other knee. Use hands to brace your body.

- Repeat with other leg.

Repetitions:
Start by doing these 10 to 15 times for each leg, depending on your present state of flexibility.

For the spine and backs of thighs:

There are two ways to perform this one as well. Choose the one that matches your flexibility, or do it both ways.

First:
sitting

- Sit on floor with legs straight out in front of you, feet together. Keep spine straight (this is difficult).

- Place hands behind neck and slowly move face-down toward the knees. Keep knees flat.

- Return to upright position.

- *Caution:* You may not be flexibile enough to get very far down toward the knees. Go as far as you can *without forcing*. The key is to *relax* down, not force down. Concentrate on your back muscles and let them relax as you bend forward. It may take a while before you can stretch out enough to get down very far, but don't try to rush it.

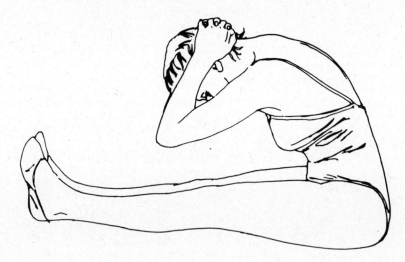

Second:
reclining

■ Lie flat out on floor, spine and body aligned.

■ Keep hands on floor, either next to hips or placed beneath buttocks.

■ Bring legs up and over your head, curling your torso to accommodate the movement, and touch toes to floor above your head.

■ You can vary this by bending the knees and placing them on the floor on either side of head.

Caution: It may be necessary at the start to support your hips with your hands. If so, do it. You may not get all the way over to touch your toes to the floor early in the game, but this will come later on.

Remember: Breathe freely and gently during this exercise.

Time: Stay in curled position for 20 to 30 breaths.

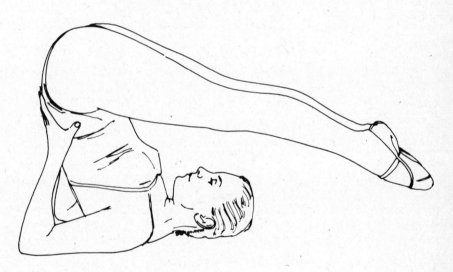

For shoulders and chest:

This will require some special care. It is easier than it looks, and is a good primer for weight training.

- Lie on back, spine aligned and knees bent.

- Bring right leg over and around the other in a winding movement, hooking right ankle behind left calf. (Men: Bring genitals forward first to avoid the crunch.)

- Extend right arm out from shoulder and place left hand on right knee.

- Bring legs over to the left side while stretching in the opposite direction with the right arm. Move arm in an arc straight up from shoulder as you stretch.

- *Time:* Do this for 20 to 30 breaths on each side of body.

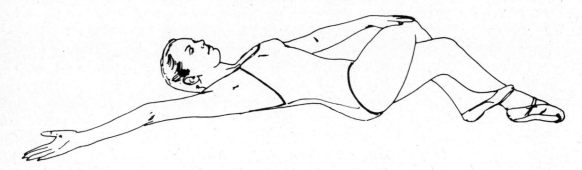

For neck

■ Sit cross-legged on floor, arms extended out from shoulders.

■ Move head around in full circles, first clockwise, then counterclockwise.

■ Stretch head back, facing ceiling.

■ Stretch face-down to touch chin to chest, elongating back of neck.

■ Stretch chin to touch first one shoulder, then the other.

For the hips:

This is also a good primer for weight lifting, since it frees up an area of the body that usually gets little stretching or meaningful exercise.

■ Sit on floor, back straight and legs spread straight out to form a "V" from your hips.

■ Raise arms straight up from shoulders toward ceiling.

■ Bring your hands down to try to touch toes. You may not be flexible enough to get all the way, so go only as far as you can along the leg.

■ *Time:* Do each move for a count of 20 to 30 breaths.

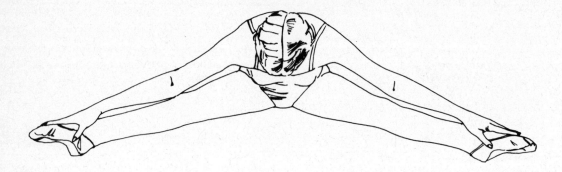

A variation on the position—some people find this easier to achieve than first position:

- Sit with legs crossed instead of straight out.

- Extend hands out in front of you, then sweep down, bringing arms backward and bending forward to touch head to floor.

For spine, chest, and psoas muscle:

What, you may ask, is the psoas muscle? It is the muscle that keeps you standing erect. If this muscle becomes jammed or doesn't function correctly, lordosis results, and you walk bent forward. This exercise, which can be performed two ways, stretches that muscle.

First:
on your back

- Make a bridge, arching chest upward and supporting body with hands and feet.

- To get into it, lie on back with knees bent, feet apart about a foot.

- Place hands over your head and palms down on floor, close in to shoulders.

- Push up with hands and feet at same time; let head drop back.

Second:
on your belly

- Lie flat on floor, face-down.

- Reach behind and grasp ankles with hands.

- Push with feet. Pull with hands to make your body rise into a bow shape. Bring head upward.

Time: Do either position for a count of 20 breaths. This may be too long for many people, since in either position it is both a feat of flexibility and a strange way to have to breathe.

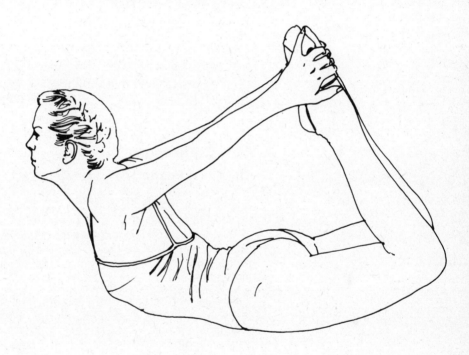

LEARNING THE EQUIPMENT

There are a lot of strange, gleaming chromium objects in your gym, waiting to eat you alive when the instructor isn't looking. These objects are weight-lifting machines and exercise apparatus—as you've already surmised. This chapter will familiarize you with the equipment you are likely to find in your gym, tell you what it does, and present the principles of using it.

The Equipment

The Sit-up Board: There are two types. One is a simple, flat, padded board with a strap at one end, where you can anchor your feet while doing sit-ups. The other has a wedge built into it to keep your knees bent during sit-ups.

In the gym, you will find several of both types of sit-up boards hooked onto a rack. The rack has about five metal rungs, so you can adjust the board at steeper angles as you strengthen your abdominal muscles.

Barbells, Dumbbells, and Weights: The unweighted *barbell* is a simple round bar of steel, often polished, and with hatchmarks to provide better gripping for your hands. It may vary in length from 5 to 7 feet. The longer ones are thicker and can carry the heavy weights needed for power lifting and advanced body building.

The bar also has collars to stabilize the weights. These collars are removable, so that you can add or subtract weights for your own strength needs. This equipment usually has a spin key that tightens it to hold the weights in place.

Some gyms now carry sets of fixed-weight barbells in varying weight classes. You cannot change these weights. You simply choose the particular barbell you need for your exercises.

Although most of the barbells you'll find are straight bars, some are curved at the places where you put your hands. These barbells are used in the same way as the straight ones, but they provide greater stability and resistance during your exercise.

Dumbbells are short versions of barbells, designed to be held in one hand only. You can affix a great deal of weight onto a dumbbell, which permits it to be used for intense workouts.

The *weight plates* are discs of iron or some other composition with holes in the middle. You load them onto the barbell just as you would place a record on a turntable. Remember to place an equal number of plates on either end of the barbell, and to include the weight of the bar itself in your calculations. (The barbell, unloaded, usually weighs about 12½ pounds, but check this out with the gym manager in case of variations.)

WORKING THE WEIGHT STACK

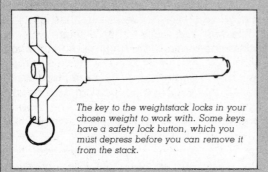

The key to the weightstack locks in your chosen weight to work with. Some keys have a safety lock button, which you must depress before you can remove it from the stack.

A weight stack is literally a stack of oblong iron bars attached to the pulley of a weight-lifting machine. Nautilus uses the same type of weight stacks as other machines.

To engage the weight stack: When you use the machine, you lift the amount of weights you've chosen from the stack. The weights are engaged as long as they are no longer resting on the stack. When engaged, the weight resistance is transferred to your muscles.

To lock in your chosen weight: Each weight bar has a keyhole.

Take the key (see illustration), press the button in the center of the handle, and insert the key into the keyhold of the appropriate weight bar. The key will pass through and lock itself into the center bar so you can lift that amount of weight during your exercise. Remember to press the button of the key when removing or inserting it; otherwise you won't be able to get it in or out.

If the key sticks: Often the center bar loses its alignment. It may be necessary to bear down on the top of the weight stack to force the key into the hole or to remove it. Sometimes the stack needs to be lifted slightly by someone who engages the weights while you insert the key. This will happen if the pulley becomes too taut or too slack.

If the key is missing: Steal one from another weight stack, or tell the management at the gym. ■

Benches: In general, the padded bench—a versatile item—is not long enough for you to lie on it full-length. Also, it is too narrow to accommodate arm movement. The bench is used primarily for doing bench-press exercises for the chest, but it is also practical for sit-down exercises—such as specialized intense workouts with dumbbells for the biceps.

Some benches are equipped with barbell stands at one end. Although this design has the heavily loaded barbell in mind, it is useful for anyone. You place the barbell on the notched stand, lie with your head in position, and remove the barbell from the stand to do bench presses. This allows you to keep the weight off your chest and avoid damage to your ribs or body as you're sitting and rising before and after the exercise.

Incline Boards: These are about 6 feet high, permanently slanted with a place for you to stand and lean back. There are several exercises you can do on this board, but most people use it primarily to do dumbbell exercises for the pectorals, shoulders, and biceps.

Decline Boards: On these, you lie with the feet anchored and the head at the lowest level. They are for intense abdominal workouts.

Hyperextension Stand: You can do two types of work on this useful item. First, you can lie face-down, with heels anchored, so you are suspended horizontally above the floor. You lower your upper body, to let your head down, and raise and lower it, strengthening the back. You can also do "full-circle" sit-ups, by sitting, letting your head go all the way back, and pulling yourself up using the abdominals.

Arm-Curl Stands: There are many variations on this theme—some are stand-ups; some are used sitting down; some are actual weight-lifting machines, complete with pulleys. The stand has a slanted armrest on which you rest your elbows and upper arms, and perform the bicep-curl exercise. This is the best way to do these curls, since your elbows are held stabilized, and you are able to isolate the biceps from being helped by the rest of your body.

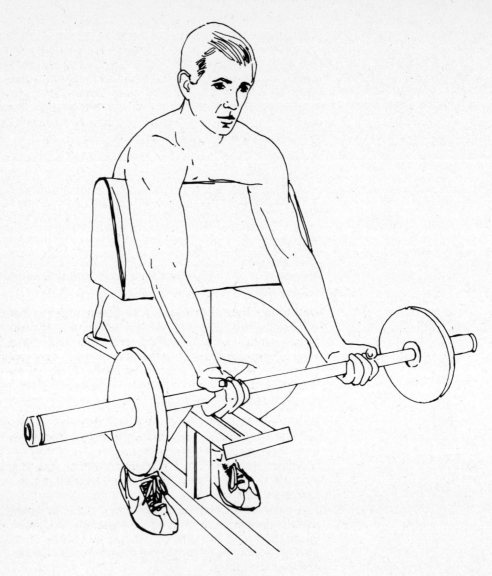

Arm-curl stand

The curl machines have a movable bar that is attached to the weight stack by pulleys. You raise and lower this bar to perform the curls.

Incline-Press Machines: These machines replace barbells for doing bench presses. The bench is placed in position into the machine so that the two handles are aligned with the pectorals. The handles are attached to weighted pulleys. You perform your exercises without having to carry barbells. This machine may be adjusted for you to perform either behind-neck presses while sitting up, or standing presses. It can also be used for triceps exercises if you face away from it and grasp the inner part of the handles.

Exercise Bikes: These are stationary bikes with one wheel in front. Otherwise they look and act exactly like a bicycle. They should have a meter on the bars and a control to adjust the resistance of the pedals so that you can vary the intensity of your workout. The meter tells you how fast and how "far" you have pedaled. If all these things are functioning properly, exercise bikes provide a fine source of aerobic exercise.

Some newer bikes are hooked up to a computerlike gauge for better accuracy and scientific aerobic training.

Calf-Raise Machine: This is a weighted machine that does not use pulleys. You stand on a pedestal, with shoulders braced against two padded projections connected to a weight stack. When you do the calf raises, you raise and lower the weights. This is a very effective machine, since it allows you to bring your heels lower than your toes, and provides good stretching for these muscles.

Leg-Press Machine: Again, this is sometimes made without pulleys; the lifting pad is attached to weight stacks—in this case there are stacks on either side. Some of these machines, however, are simpler in construction, and you must load the weights directly on top of the board that you raise and lower with your feet.

A backrest is provided so that you can lie down, with your feet up against the lifting pad. You push the weighted pad or board upward to exercise your thighs and buttocks. You can also do toe raises while the legs are fully extended to exercise the calves.

Leg and Thigh Machine: This is a table that has padded bars and weighted pulleys. One padded bar is projected at a level higher than the table—for leg curls to exercise the backs of the thighs. The other bar is below the table, and you sit on the edge of the table, hook your ankles behind it, and do thigh extensions.

Some of these machines have spindles that allow you to add or remove weight plates; others are connected to the pulley and weight stack, and you adjust the weights with a key.

Weight Stacks: These are a stack of flat weights, with notch holes provided so you can insert a key at the weight you want. Each plate lower increases the weight you will work with by 10 pounds.

Leg Lift Stand: This is for doing leg raises while you support your arms on elbow pads. Your feet are held about 6 inches off the floor, while your upper body is supported in a stable position. These exercises are good for the abdominals and the obliques (love handles). The stand would be more versatile if you could also do shoulder dips, but there is no space for that on this machine.

The Multiple-Station Machine: This is sometimes referred to as a "Universal" machine, although Universal is only one of the manufacturers that makes them. They combine several machines in a single central construction, so you can do just about all of your exercises with this one machine. You move around the various stations on it and perform thigh extensions, arm exercises, overhead presses, and so forth. Since the versatility of these machines varies from gym to gym, it is necessary to be instructed on how to use the one at your own health club. The principles of weight lifting apply, however, no matter how varied they are. These machines do not do anything different from regular weights, but they are much more convenient and relieve you of the necessity of balancing and of carrying free weights. If you can do your exercises on them, this is recommended, especially for beginners, since the safety factor is increased.

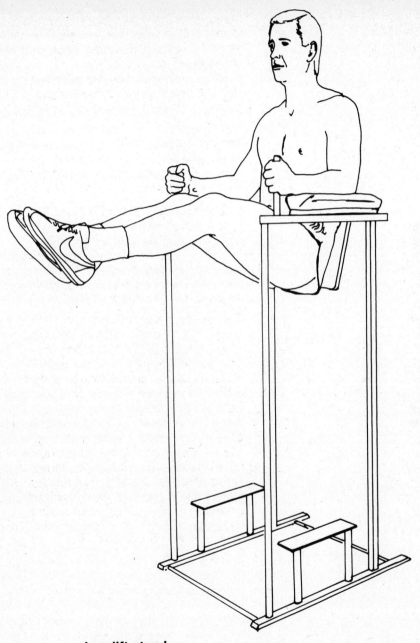

Leg lift stand

[145]

The Seated Leg Machine: This machine may be found either on some of the multiple-station machines or separately. Using it, you perform the same leg exercises as in a deep-knee bend or using the leg press lying on your back. The seat is angled, so you sit to push your legs against the resisting weight. It is safer than doing the deep-knee bend, but not as easy to execute as either the thigh-extension/leg-curl machine, or the leg press.

Rowing Machines: You will have no trouble identifying these even if you have never laid eyes on a canoe. The machine has a floor-level platform, a seat and a footrest, and two oars to row nowhere. Since there are different types around, be sure to get instructions on how to use the one at your gym. Rowing is an aerobic exercise and is also excellent for toning the whole body—especially the shoulders, arms, and back. For most people the treadmill or the exercise bike is preferable, since either one is easier for the nonathlete to use without instruction.

Hip Exercisers: These are favored in women's gyms and may vary in design and use. Essentially, you sit with your knees fastened or held in some way and perform resistance exercises that place work on the hips and thighs. The hip exercisers generally work by your opening and closing the thighs against resistance, and can be very effective for trimming those areas.

Twisters: While in principle the platforms employed here sound handy, their effectiveness is questionable. You stand on a platform which moves back and forth in a circular motion. You stabilize your hands to hold the torso stationary, and do the twist. The purpose is to whittle the waist. This exercise is one of the most effective for flattening tum-tums, but there are better ways to do it. Preferably, the lower body is stationary while you twist the upper body—giving better control and a better stretch. And without a platform, you can't fall off.

Roller Machines: Someone made a lot of money selling these worthless items to every health club in the country, which is certainly proof that P. T. Barnum knew what he was talking about. These are moving barrels that turn and turn. Instead of slats, they have polished wooden dowels (rollers) that are supposed to break up fat and make you trim and slim. Since the human body doesn't work that way, and since you can hurt yourself if you don't use the machine correctly, we suggest you consider it as a thing to look at, to admire—a sort of perpetual-motion machine—while you're waiting for your turn at the real exercise machines.

Treadmills: These are machines with moving belts that you can run on without going anywhere. There are handrails that you use for support in order not to get carried off the side; these are great for aerobic conditioning, or even for five-minute warm-up runs prior to working out. Generally, they should have adjustments for different speeds, and on some you may even be able to angle the belt for an "uphill" jog.

EATING ALL THE WAY

Part 1

No exercise program can bring you meaningful improvements without a nutritional program to back it up. If your diet consists mostly of carbohydrates and is low in protein, it will be almost impossible to achieve the muscle building or toning you want.

If you do not eat properly, exercise may deteriorate your body instead of building it up. You may become fatigued easily and suffer excessive soreness after your workouts. At the worst, you may experience dizziness or faint nausea, simply because you are not taking in the fuel that provides the extra energy demanded by your body during intense exercise. Before you jump into a heavy exercise plan, you should evaluate your whole way of eating to determine exactly what you are taking in and how it affects your body. Most people do not think about what they eat. They may be eating only two meals a day and still can't seem to shed that excess roll of fat around the waist. They are convinced they are on a well-balanced diet, and are puzzled. Clearly, a close evaluation of your diet is needed.

Nutritional Guidelines and Recommendations

The nutrition information and recommendations in this chapter are based on material provided by A Health Affair, a supernutrition clinic in Los Angeles, California. Donald R. Dickenson, Ph.D., and Garyx Zimmerman, D.C., who operate the clinic, have had much success in the analysis and treatment of disorders caused by nutritional inadequacies. Their nutritional philosophy is based on the latest research available.

Many people may be startled by the amount of eggs, beef, and high-cholesterol foods listed in sample menus in this chapter. Although cholesterol is often portrayed as a culprit, the fact is that it is essential to life. Even if you do not eat cholesterol, your body will produce the amount it needs. The body uses cholesterols in certain protective ways that can, however, lead to an undesirable buildup on the artery walls. This condition occurs when the abundance of refined sugars in the diet causes lesions on the artery walls, and the body uses cholesterols to "coat" these lesions. Whether or not you eat cholesterol, your body will still manufacture the cholesterols and use them for this purpose. The true culprit is the refined sugar and starch in highly processed foods.

As for eating low-saturated or high-saturated cholesterol foods, it has been shown that the body digests hard fats less easily, so these cholesterols are passed out of the system undigested, as opposed to the more easily digested "light" oils. The point to be made is that much misinformation exists on the subject of cholesterol. Low-saturated oils are not necessarily "good guys," and nutritious foods containing saturated fats are not automatically to be avoided.

The people at A Health Affair operate on the basis of studies that indicate that high cholesterol levels in the blood are not caused by eating high-cholesterol foods. This is a simple statement to make about a fairly complicated and controversial subject, but it has been shown to the author's satisfaction, through his experience with A Health Affair, that the nutritional

▶

recommendations made here are effective, safe, and beneficial to persons who have embarked on a weight training program. However, the author realizes that these are controversial recommendations and that you should ultimately be guided by the advice of a physician who has examined you and understands your own physical condition.

If you already have a condition of high serum cholesterol or arteriosclerosis, then cutting down on dietary cholesterol may be recommended as part of your treatment. It should also be noted that certain types of exercise have a direct beneficial effect on lowering blood cholesterol levels.

The author feels that this type of high-energy, low-carbohydrate diet is the most reasonable method of obtaining proper nutrition for energy needs on a shaping-up program, as well as providing for the maintenance of the internal functions of the body. We believe that the low-calorie fat-loss diets are, in fact, not suitable to meet the kind of energy demands made on the body by any strenuous exercise program.

The author also would like to stress that there is no single approach to fitness, nutrition, and health that can claim to be the only way for everyone. There are many roads to fitness. We feel that the nutritional program here is extremely suitable to a fitness program and, with certain modifications, provides a lifetime plan of sensible eating for most people. It should be stressed that we are providing a direction here for a nutritional program that will best serve a program of exercise designed to build the muscles and provide the energy required for an intense, concentrated program of exercise. Some people may find that they do not require excessive amounts of protein in the diet, nor do they want to ingest foods containing large amounts of cholesterol and fat. ∎

Protein Power

Of the three basic food groups—proteins, carbohydrates, and fats—the most important to a shaping-up program is protein—the amino acids. Protein has several important functions that directly affect your body during this time:

■ *Organ and muscle building.* Protein, which is comprised of amino acids, is required to manufacture new cells for the muscles and skin and to maintain the functioning organs of the body. A deficiency of protein in the diet hinders this cell-building function, and our bodies work at a lower level of efficiency. For strength training, protein is vital, since you cannot build powerful muscles without adequate protein. For muscle and skin tone, the amino acids are also necessary.

■ *Energy.* Protein is responsible for maintaining your blood-sugar levels. When you have a protein deficiency—even for a short time—your blood-sugar level drops and you may experience excessive fatigue. People who are consistently deprived of protein often experience a chronic low-blood-sugar level, called hypoglycemia, characterized by dizziness or fainting spells due to the diversion of protein from body-building to fueling the body. On a milder level, a protein-poor diet may cause a constant craving for sweets.

There are two kinds of protein food: the *complete* protein food, or *high-quality* protein, and the *incomplete* protein food. Because the body cannot manufacture certain amino acids, you must obtain them through food. Complete protein food provides all nine of these aminos—called *essential* amino acids. Foods which provide some or none of these essential aminos are considered incomplete sources of protein, or low-quality protein foods. You must eat foods containing these essential aminos *every day* for your body to function at its proper capacity.

The foods which contain the complete essential aminos are meat, eggs, fish, milk and some milk products, and some types of nuts. Many foods may be high in protein and may even contain larger amounts of incomplete protein, but they do not complete the picture. Foods such as grains, beans, and peanuts are sources of protein and can maintain important body functions such as growth and maintenance, but are still not high-quality protein sources.

The essential aminos that must be obtained through food are histidine, isoleucine, leucine, lysine, tryptophan, valine, methionine, phenylalanine, and threonine. We list them here so you can check the labels of protein supplements to learn which essential aminos are available in the package.

How Much?

The body is able to assimilate only about 26 grams of protein at a single shot. This amount is not adequate for one adult's daily nutritional requirements, so you must eat several meals throughout the day to absorb all the protein you need. The National Research Council's food and nutrition board publishes a list of Recommended Daily Allowances, which shows the grams of protein required by humans according to body weight. It says, for instance, that a 155-pound man needs 56 grams of protein a day. The allowance is based on a computation of less than one-half gram of protein per pound of human body weight—and most nutritionists emphatically state that this is not enough.

The food and nutrition board agrees and suggests that it is important to eat *more* protein than this recommended amount to insure assimilation. Because of inefficiencies in digestion, your body does not utilize all the amino acids you eat. Also, since these aminos are assimilated in percentage ratios to each other, you must eat much more protein than is recommended to guarantee that you get the maximum benefits from your diet.

It is not likely that your body can obtain 100 percent digestive efficiency, but you can increase nutritional benefits by providing enough raw material for your body to work with.

As a rule of thumb to determine how much protein you should take in for basic normal activity, compute one-half gram of protein for each pound of body weight.

If you are thinner than you want to be, add protein to the basic computation. For example, if you are a 6-foot man and weigh about 145 pounds, you may have computed that you need 73 grams of protein a day. If you want to be sure you are digesting that much, add about 15 grams—about 5 grams a meal. If you want to bulk up, start "pumping" protein in large amounts of about 100 grams a day—adding a fourth meal if necessary—to fuel the growth you want.

If you are very heavy, say 300 pounds, your protein computation would come out to 150 grams a day. Since your true weight would be less—and if you know generally what weight you would be if you weren't obese—compute your protein needs on the lower weight. Because protein intake won't interfere with fat loss, you can still maintain a high level of protein in your diet and cut way down on carbohydrates to lose weight. In any event, make sure that you take in enough protein to keep your blood sugar up and your craving for sweets down.

Carbohydrates

Carbohydrates (we'll also refer to them as "carbs") are basically sugars of various forms. They are useful in the diet to provide quick energy. Foods that contain carbohydrates can be either healing or harmful agents, depending on their form. Certain fruits, for example, contain minerals and vitamins we need to aid certain internal functions. Some fresh fruit can be extremely soothing and nourishing during times of illness or stress. But refined sugar is a sweetener without any nutritional value. Furthermore, it acts as a stimulant, much like caffeine, using up the body's reserves of energy. For someone who is trying to build up the body, most sugars act as a hindrance.

Many avant-garde food people these days think that carbs are not even necessary in the diet to any great extent, since our lifestyles don't require using the energy they provide. Since they are mostly converted and stored as fat in the tissue and blood, it appears to be best to eliminate this excess from the diet altogether. Certain primitive societies, such as the Masai tribe in Africa, maintain a high-fat/high-protein diet with little or no carbohydrates. Heart disease and cholesterol problems are unknown among them.

You must do a lot of intense physical exertion in a very brief span of time to use up a significant amount of energy from carbohydrates. People engaged in rigorous running and aerobic sports do use up these carbs, but people taking moderate exercise or merely performing normal daily activities at work and at home have no opportunity to burn them up.

It should be noted here that weight lifting, despite the exertion demanded by that sport, does not use up a lot of carbohydrates. For this reason, people shaping up through a weight-training type of exercise must limit carbohydrates and increase the other two food groups to accommodate their program.

Fats and Misconceptions

The third group, fat, has been treated as a culprit for many years in medical and nutritional circles. But fats become important for energy during a low-carbohydrate regimen, and they should be viewed as part of a well-rounded eating plan.

Fat in the diet provides weight trainers with long-term energy and takes a long time to be digested in the body. Because of this, it can furnish a "bedrock" of energy to sustain you between meals. It also satisfies the appetite quickly, and prevents excessive hunger pangs that send you searching through the refrigerator between meals.

Part 2

Figuring Food

Most people don't really analyze what they eat. They have a general idea that they either eat a lot or don't eat much. There is only one way to figure out what you are eating and in what amounts, and that is to make a list of everything you eat when you eat it. If you are keeping a shaping-up notebook, as suggested earlier in this book, it is time to start recording each mouthful of food you take.

We asked three friends to do this for us. They each kept lists of their eating habits for three days—three days being a long-enough time to provide a valid overview of their usual patterns. Here are some samplings, showing the food they ate and an approximation of the proteins and carbohydrates they were taking in. Since each one of them was having a problem losing fat, they had some surprises when they began to examine their mealtimes. All three complained about energy loss, depression, or irritability at times.

SAMPLE 1:
William, age 39, weight 155 pounds. Complaint: a roll of fat
around the waist that wouldn't go away despite regular
running and gym work, and a lack of muscle tone.

One day's food intake:

ITEM	PROTEIN (GRAMS)	CARBS (GRAMS)
1 plum		7.
2 boiled eggs	26.	.8
2 slices cinnamon toast		27.
Coffee, with half-and-half		1.2
2 hot dogs (no bread)	16.	6.
Diet 7-Up		7.
7 cookies		50.
Chicken cutlets	28.	
Zucchini		2.
Boiled potato		23.
1 apple		18.
Cranberry/apricot juice		34.

The total amount of carbs for this day was 176 grams, as
opposed to only about 70 grams of protein—below the
Recommended Daily Allowances for his weight by about 10
grams.

SAMPLE 2:
John, age 36, weight 196 pounds. Complaint: too much body fat all around.

One day's food intake:

ITEM	PROTEIN (GRAMS)	CARBS (GRAMS)
1 glass grapefruit juice		20.
2 eggs	26.	.8
1 slice French toast	12.	14.
3 pieces bacon	12.	
Fruit salad		60.
Coffee		.4
Potato salad (½ pound)		32.
Fish	30.	
Jell-O		18.
Coffee		.4
5 Lite beers		13.
Canned soup		11.
Tomatoes, onions		8.
Chicken and prosciutto	35.	
5 bread sticks		30.
Coffee		.4
"Green drink" (crème de menthe/ vodka)		15.

The total amount of carbs taken in was 223 grams, which effectively buried the adequate 115 grams of protein he ate.

SAMPLE 3:
Cynthia, age 27, weight 101 pounds.
Here we are presenting all three days' food intake since Cynthia is a rather unusual case. She is not overweight—in fact, she is fashionably slim—but her carbohydrate intake is

overbalanced in relation to her protein percentage. She does have a problem with energy loss and minor fatigue during the day. Although the carbs are not causing a fat problem, she exhibits signs of periodic low blood sugar and has the desire for sweets that attends that condition. Because she is careful to concentrate on "natural" foods, whole grains, and honey-made sweets, she feels she is maintaining a good diet. In fact, she *does* get a good deal of protein, but not enough of the high-quality protein foods to make a balanced diet.

Cynthia could embark on an exercise program with her present diet, but she would find the results slow in coming and might suffer periods of intense fatigue. Because of her low body weight, she would not need to increase her protein intake by much, since she would need a base of only about 52 to 56 grams of complete protein a day to maintain a normal, active lifestyle.

ITEM	PROTEIN (GRAMS)	CARBS (GRAMS)
Day One:		
1 slice whole wheat bread		11.5
1 tsp. jam		6.
Coffee with milk/sugar		10.
Chili	24.	40.
Small salad (lettuce/ tomato)		2.5
1 slice whole wheat bread		11.5
Butter		
Pear		25.
Tortellini/tomato sauce		40.
Salad		
Plum		7.
Total:	24.	153.5

ITEM	PROTEIN (GRAMS)	CARBS (GRAMS)
Day Two:		
1 slice whole wheat bread/jam		11.5
6 oz. apricot juice		27.
Cheese sandwich	12.	23.
Pear and halvah		38.
Coffee with milk/sugar		10.
Nuts	13.	13.
Meat loaf	24.	10.
Rice		20.
Tomatoes/olive oil		2.5
Plum and orange		23.
Total:	49.	178.
Day Three:		
1 slice date-nut bread		12.
Coffee with milk/sugar		10.
Split pea soup		42.
Cheese sandwich	12.	23.
2 plums		14.
Vegetable soup		13.
Lamb stew	24.	22.
Strawberry tart		20.
Total:	36.	156.

Although Cynthia takes in a fair amount of complete protein foods on a daily basis, never does she attain the minimum amount recommended for her body weight. Since she does not gain weight, it can be surmised that she does not need to cut her carbs—most of them come from properly nutritional sources, very few from refined sugar—but only to increase the amount of complete protein in her meals. She should make sure that she gets some complete protein—about 15 to 20 grams in her case—at every meal, which she is not doing now.

The reasons we started off this section with these samples was to show (a) how you can take a reading of your own daily food intake, (b) how much the average American relies on carbohydrates as his main source of nutrition, and (c) how far below your minimum protein needs you can get and not know it. All of these people thought their diets were reasonably well balanced. None of them thought they were ingesting an unusual amount of carbs and sugars. None of them ate more than three meals a day.

When keeping a record of your food intake, use both a protein and a carbohydrate counter, which are easily available in bookstores, department stores, health food stores, and at some supermarket checkout counters. For the first three days, don't try to change anything; just keep a record of every mouthful you eat or drink. It is difficult to gauge fat since it is present in so many forms in almost all foods, including vegetables, but for this purpose fat is not important.

If you do have excess body fat, it is almost certain that you are absorbing at least 150 grams of carbohydrates and not using them up in your daily expenditure of energy. If you are underweight, it is probable that your diet is low in carbs, and perhaps very low in daily protein intake as well. Some people, however, are normally thin and may be keeping a well-balanced diet. The telling points are this or that person's energy and psychological mood. If both are high, he or she is probably getting all the nutrition needed. Some slender people are able to consume large amounts of carbohydrates and still not get fat. They obviously utilize the carbs. But thinness is no indication that your diet is adequate in protein. The only way to tell is by looking closely and computing it.

Part 3

Eating for the Gym

Before getting into a weight-loss or weight-gain program, it is important to keep a record of what you eat for the first month at least. If you then make "spot-checks" to be sure you don't slip out of the program, you should be able to maintain the new eating plan as naturally as you did the old ways.

When planning a new regime, remember that you are going to gravitate to the same type of high-protein eating plan whether you are trying to gain weight or lose it. The best eating plan for shaping up provides the balance of protein, carbs, and fats mentioned earlier.

Sample Eating Plan for One Day

The suggestions of this plan are intended to provide guidelines for typical meals during your program. We do not suggest that you eat only the foods listed here. You may not like eggs or ham; you may not want to eat so many eggs during the day. We want to make the point that eating complete protein foods in comparable amounts is necessary on this eating plan. You have a wide choice of foods: chicken or turkey; lamb, pork, or other meat products, such as liver; fish is a wonderful source of protein, although the cost of fish makes it almost a delicacy these days. Canned tuna and salmon, however, provide high-quality protein meals at a minimal cost. Milk and cheese are also excellent sources, although their carbohydrate content may be too high for dieters.

Breakfast: 3 eggs
Ham
Rye thins, buttered or with cream cheese
Hot beverage, no sugar

Lunch: ½ pound sliced turkey
Tomatoes, celery, lettuce, with mayonnaise
Cottage cheese
Rye thins
1 peach

Snack: 8-oz. can tuna or salmon
or 1 pint milk

Dinner: 12 oz. steak (or chicken, or some other meat)
Salad, with lettuce, tomatoes, half an avocado, dressing
½ cup strawberries

This sample eating plan would provide adequate protein needs for an active day of work and exercise, furnish enough variety to make the meals interesting, and still keep the carbohydrate count hovering around 40-plus grams—low enough to cause the body to utilize fat stored in the tissue.

You may like your carbs in different ways, however. If you want to have orange juice in the morning, for example, then you won't have the fruit or the milk later on. It may not be necessary to have the snack, either, although it is a good idea at the start to "pump" protein into your system in order to ward off food cravings. Eating frequent meals also has the effect of initiating the metabolic process that burns off body fat. If you eat fewer meals, you may lose fat at a slower rate, because with less food intake this process does not occur as many times during the day.

This type of eating plan is attractive to people who are "compulsive eaters." The hardest part of weight-loss diets is to cut out the mechanics of eating whenever the mood strikes. The amount of food, plus the frequent number of times when you should eat, makes this plan easy to go with. When the protein gets a chance to do its job of nourishing you, you find yourself thinking less and less about wanting to eat, and many overeaters have complained about the new difficulty of "forcing" themselves to eat so much.

Skinny people have a more difficult time with this plan, since they are not used to eating so much or so frequently. The difficulty is often caused by habit, and getting onto a regular eating regimen may spark the appetite. Because there may be a medical reason for inadequate eating habits, we suggest checking with a doctor if you think you have a problem.

But the best part of this fat-control plan is that you never have to go hungry again. The food is there in adequate quantities, and you don't have to worry about overeating as long as you limit the carbs.

There are people who already live on a very limited carbohydrate diet and never have the desire for more—except on special occasions. Many formerly obese people make the change and experience no problem keeping the carbs way down for an indefinite time.

Many people feel that it is unhealthy to cut down on carbohydrates for an extended period of time. In fact, there are good and bad carbs. Fresh vegetables provide an excellent source of carbohydrates, as do certain whole grains, potatoes, and other unrefined foods. The villains are refined sugar, refined flour (which is used in most breads and baked goods), and processed oils. Carbohydrates provide energy to fuel the body in its functions, but eating indiscriminate amounts of carbohydrates may cause obesity, tissue damage, or both. A high-protein diet allows you to lower your carbohydrate intake, because you are taking in the amino acids required for body-cell maintenance and still have enough food fuel for energy needs.

If you go on a high-protein, low-carbohydrate eating plan, you will be able to consume meat, fish, and eggs in quantities that are limited only by your ability to eat them. When the body's natural turn-off point is functioning, it becomes difficult to take in too much food. The usual complaint about this diet plan is that the person gets tired of eating so much. Yet the fat is disappearing.

As the fat goes, you will experience a weight loss. Later on—especially with men—the muscle growth causes either a stabilization of the weight loss or an increase, since muscle tissue is heavier than fat.

Reactions

When you start on a high-protein, low-carbohydrate plan, certain adverse reactions may occur as you progress. You may feel fatigued, upset, cranky, and ravenous. You may or may not lose inches or weight. The reason for some of these reactions is that your body, accustomed to carbohydrates for fuel, is "missing" them, and is very upset about it. By withholding carbs from the diet, you are forcing your body to switch over to using the energy stored in the fat tissue. However, you may not experience any negative reactions at all.

You may find that you are losing your desire for sweets and sugars. It is possible, though, that this won't happen in the early weeks. If the desire for sweets persists for an unusually long time—say over two months—it may be advisable to have your doctor give you a sugar-tolerance test to determine if hypoglycemia or some other sugar imbalance is present. If you suspect you have this chronic problem already, it is best to find out at the start, since it may act as a hindrance to your shaping-up program and inhibit muscle building and toning.

Carbs versus Calories

Why should you cut carbs instead of calories? The basic answer is that on a strenuous exercise program you need the calories for energy, and you will be using them during your workouts. Cutting carbs does not deprive your body of the energy it needs for all this new work. By providing a fat-loss opportunity through less carbs, and by still taking in the amount of food you need, you will strike a happy balance between full stomach and slim waist.

What Foods Should You Choose?

There are certain foods on this eating plan that you can eat in large amounts, others that you should avoid until your fat level is down where you want it, and still others that you can enjoy in limited amounts. The suggestions that follow are intended to guide you. If you have any doubt about the carbohydrate content of anything, check it out with a carb counter.

Eat All You Want: Meat; fish; eggs; vegetables such as the green leafies; string beans; zucchini; broccoli; cauliflower; celery; eggplant; any of the green or yellow vegetables.

Eat Limited Amounts: Cheese; yogurt; nuts; milk; tomatoes; avocados; some melons; fruit; carrots; berries.

Eliminate: Sugar, and any prepared or processed food made with sugar (including some roasted nuts); corn syrups; high-carb sweeteners such as honey, alcoholic beverages including beer, wine, and liqueurs.

Count Carbs Carefully: Grains; corn and corn products; breads; baked goods; high-carb fruits including grapefruit; anything made with wheat flour; kasha; oatmeal; breakfast cereals; rice; potatoes; all starchy foods.

[163]

Spices and Herbs

Spices and herbs are almost essential to this type of eating program, to prevent the food from tasting like chalk after a certain point. Green, leafy herbs can be used liberally. The "hotter" spices—such as pepper, paprika, chili powder—generally can also be used, since they are low in carbohydrates, almost to the trace level, and you would not be using enough of them at a given time to make a difference. Curry powder, however, must be counted, since it may contain as many as 5 grams of carbs per teaspoon. In general, you're safe not counting carbs in spices and herbs, and using them in your low-carbohydrate meals can keep you faithful by making the food you eat more palatable.

A Special Note for Vegetarians

Vegetarians normally need to make a special effort to obtain their daily requirements of complete protein foods. Vegetarians who allow themselves eggs and milk products, of course, have no problem gauging protein at all and can shape up as easily as, if not better than, meat eaters. When gauging vegetable protein sources, you must know which amino acids are present in any given source, and in what amounts; then mix and match foods to obtain your complete complement of essential amino acids. Except for certain nuts, there are hardly any non-animal foods that are sources of complete protein. Since roasting procedures destroy some amino acids, these sources may be dubious at times. Peanuts are not considered sources of complete protein, although peanut butter is currently being advertised as high-quality protein. Soybeans, while they are technically high in protein, require so much cooking that their protein content is diminished by the time you are ready to consume them.

Other Values

Certain protein foods are considered higher-quality sources of amino acids than others. Eggs, for example, are digested and assimilated more easily by the human body than any other protein food. Chicken is another high-quality source because it is highest in protein per unit weight than other meats. Turkey is also high in protein and is an excellent, easy-to-digest source of complete protein. Beef is high in protein but is not as easily assimilated as the above sources; pork and lamb, the other popular meats, are about the same as beef on these levels. Organ meats are not popular with everyone, but if you like them, you'll have another source of protein to tap.

Milk, cheese, and other milk products are excellent protein sources but are high in carbs. An 8-ounce container of yogurt carries between 17 to 32 carbs, depending on its fruit content. Cottage cheese, another popular item, is much lower, carrying about 6 or 7 grams per cup. Cream cheese is extremely low, containing 1 gram or less per ounce. Even flavored cream cheeses are very low in carbs.

Whole milk contains less carbs per quart than skim milk, so for low-carb dieters, whole milk is preferred. The reason for this is because fat is replaced in skim milk by a higher volume of the carbohydrate-containing part of the milk. There is no loss of protein in skim milk, however.

Vitamins

One of the difficult areas to analyze for oneself is vitamin deficiency. A nutritionist or a physician should be able to determine this by examining your diet and your complaints.

Everyone is in agreement that vitamins are good for you. There are certain vitamin deficiencies that may affect your shaping-up program. Lack of vitamins can cause fatigue, muscle weakness, and poor appetite. We're providing a list of some pertinent vitamin deficiencies that affect shaping up. It is not a complete list of *all* vitamin deficiencies, just the ones pertaining to an exercise program.

LACK OF...	CAUSES...
Vitamin A	Loss of appetite; frequent colds; dry skin; roughness and acne; dry hair and dandruff; loss of smell; fatigue.
C	Broken capillaries; bleeding gums; nosebleed; slow healing; shortness of breath; swollen, painful joints; easy bruising.
D	(Unusual deficiency; usually combined with calcium and hydrochloric acid.) Postural problems; fragile bones; poorly developed muscles. In adults: softening of bones; numbness; spasms and tingling of muscles.
E	Abnormal fatty tissues in muscles; increased need for oxygen; varicose veins; dry skin; muscle atrophy; premature aging; low semen level in men.
Biotin (B$_7$)	Muscle pain; poor appetite; dry skin; lack of energy; sleeplessness.
Folic Acid	Poor growth; gray hair; gastrointestinal disturbances; can result in anemia.
Inositol	Constipation; eczema; hair loss; high blood cholesterol.
Niacin (B$_3$)	Muscle weakness; general fatigue; no appetite; indigestion; skin eruptions and small chancres; insomnia; vomiting; headaches; depression; tension; tender gums.

LACK OF ...	CAUSES ...
PABA	Fatigue; irritability; depression; nervousness; headaches; digestive disorders; constipation.
Pangamic acid (B_{15})	Diminished oxygen to cells; heart disease; glandular and nervous disorders.
Pantothenic acid (B_5)	Muscle cramps; abdominal pain; vomiting; restlessness; "bum" feet; sensitivity to insulin.

Mineral deficiencies are discovered accurately only through certain analytical laboratory techniques. There are many things that can upset a mineral balance in the body, but much of it is caused by the chemicals we breathe in our polluted air. Some minerals can be depleted by consumption of coffee and alcohol—just as some vitamins can be depleted by alcohol, caffeine, smoking, and, especially, drugs. We are listing here some symptoms of certain mineral deficiencies that may affect a shaping-up program.

LACK OF ...	CAUSES ...
Iron	Anemia.
Manganese	Failure of muscle coordination; dizziness; paralysis.
Potassium	Impairment of neuromuscular function; irregular heartbeat; muscle cramps.
Silenium	Premature aging.
Zinc	Fatigue; decreased alertness; susceptibility to infection or injuries. (Calcium and magnesium are also important because they affect muscular-contraction development.)

These lists should be used only as a guide to seeking professional help if you have any of these symptoms. A nutritional almanac would carry a complete listing of all vitamins and mineral deficiencies, as well as indicating which ones affect the other.

Minerals and vitamins act in a proportionary balance in the body, just as protein does. This means that you need certain percentages of minerals so that they can function properly in your system. A lack or an overbalance of one mineral may cause a deficiency or an overbalance of another. If you suspect a mineral imbalance in your system, consult a doctor with a nutritional orientation, or a professional nutritionist.

The taking of daily multiple vitamins as a supplement to your diet is recommended, since these are generally balanced formulas, although most popular formulations often exclude vitamins that many nutritionists feel are essential to total good health.

Protein Supplements

When on a muscle-building program, many people wonder if they should include protein supplements in their diet to guarantee getting the needed amounts. In some cases, protein supplements are useful, although most people will find they don't really need them for energy or muscle building over the long run.

A young person, under twenty-five years of age, may not ever need protein supplements. He or she is still in the developing stage and makes better use of the food that is ingested. People in this age group usually don't have much trouble with low appetite either, and tend to eat often and indiscriminately. Their systems can handle it, but even they can't utilize an overabundance of carbohydrates unless they are extremely active.

Once you are in your late twenties and early thirties, your body naturally starts to use up less of the food you eat, and less efficiently. If you don't readjust your eating habits, and continue the indiscriminate overeating patterns you engaged in early in life, you will find yourself having problems with fatty tissue and looking older than you are. You need fewer carbohydrates during these years even if you are more active, because your metabolism is not burning up extra carbs in the growing process.

During your over-thirty adulthood, the switch should be made to eating foods that serve your current body functions. You are not growing, you are maintaining what has been developed. To do this, protein is necessary. And you must take your meals in more balanced, disciplined ways to keep that maintenance functioning efficiently. Your food is now used less for energy and more for organic function.

If you are starting an exercise program, you will need extra protein to build more muscle cells and still maintain the adult body functions. If you do not provide enough nourishment, the body will have to cheat some organic functions to serve the increased energy demands made by your new exercise program. In this event, protein supplements to your diet are useful.

People who are extremely thin and want to add bulk to their frames can make good use of protein supplements for two reasons: because the added protein will help build up the extra cells needed for muscle growth, and because thin people often have poor appetites. A lack of protein in the diet can lead to loss of appetite (among other causes), and the extra amino acids should help enhance their desire for more nourishment.

People who are extremely obese often have poor digestion, and since they are not able to utilize the food they eat very efficiently, the extra protein from supplements provides the boost they need.

What Kind of Protein Supplements?

A few years ago many people were taking liquid protein—predigested amino acids that were utilized 100 percent by the body. The scandal that followed on the heels of some unhealthy weight-loss situations caused these supplements to disappear pretty thoroughly from the market. Needless to say, we are not recommending that you search for some leftover bottles of this stuff.

There is a new type of protein supplement which comes in capsule form and is superior to any others now available. It is called free-form amino acid and is formulated in a way to be assimilated in the balanced ratios by which your body would use these aminos. It is extremely expensive—about 20 cents a capsule—and is often taken in doses of five to twenty 740-milligram capsules per meal. This amount is usual for cases of serious protein deficiency or super bodybuilding. The supplement is distributed only through doctors and nutritionists.

Powdered protein supplements are the most popular with health food people and bodybuilders. Generally they are made from food and include vitamins and minerals as well as protein. Because of this they need to be digested; and you do not utilize them completely. However, they are still an effective source of protein. The problem arises from the fact that they contain carbohydrates, which must be accounted for, and have to be mixed with juice or some other liquid— another source of carbohydrates and calories.

Sometimes these protein supplements do not provide a full complement of the essential amino acids, so make sure before you buy them that you are getting a high-quality supplement.

Brewer's yeast, dessicated liver, and wheat germ also act as protein supplements; they provide B vitamins, among others, and are favored sources of nutrition as well.

It should be remembered through all this that protein supplements are just that—supplements. They are not meant to substitute for food, although some people try to do that. They should be used only as enhancers and boosters and to insure your protein assimilation.

How Often Should You Take Protein Supplements?

If you do not eat large amounts of protein at any meal— meaning below the 25 grams per meal that your system can digest—you should be including some sort of supplement for at least one of those meals. If you are extremely active, are very thin, or have problems eating regularly, you should take it more than once, whether with your meals or as an in-between boost. If you do not have time for a meal but do have time to make a fast drink with a protein supplement, it is better to take the supplement than to forgo eating altogether. This is especially true if you are on your way to a social function where you will be drinking. The protein will fortify you in advance and protect your blood-sugar level to a certain degree.

It is not recommended that you ever come to depend on the protein-drink snack as a substitute for meals. If you lead a superactive life and have great energy needs, however, this snack as a regular part of your day may enhance your energy level. It certainly makes a reasonable substitute for coffee-and-Danish-pastry breaks.

How much protein you should take at a time depends on how much is provided by the supplement itself. Because of the extra fat-causing nutrients in the supplement, you will necessarily have to consider all things when you're making your decision. If you are on a fat-loss program, you will have to count carbohydrates or calories and include them in your overall intake for the day. Two major manufacturers of these protein supplements are Hoffman Products, York, Pennsylvania; and Weider, of Woodland Hills, California.

A Question of Attitude

A friend of mine who went on the shaping-up program and eating plan in this book once told me that he knew when he was over the hump. He had started at 250 pounds and got down to 195 pounds and was loving it.

"I was working out at the gym," he said, "doing the arm exercises. I was really working hard that day and really getting into it. By this time I was almost at the end of the workout, really wet and really pushing. Then I got kind of high, and was suddenly able to go that extra couple of reps. I knew at that point I would never go back ... I knew it. I'd never go back to being fat or eating the way I used to."

I wouldn't be telling this story if he hadn't been right. Two years later he still hasn't slipped, even though his work schedule has virtually stopped his gym visits. It is true that when you do achieve this kind of reshaping, something also takes place in your mental approach. You start to think like the new person you've become, and you don't go back. Even if you fluctuate periodically, the curve stays within the new frame of reference.

The ideal is to reach the point where you do not slip and do not vary. To get to the shape you want and hold it—right there! And once you arrive at that point, there is no reason not to maintain. After all, the hard work is already done ... the rest is simply maintenance.

MOVING ON UP

Christopher Reeve shaped up for his *Superman* movie role in about two months. He could shape up that quickly because he did not have to lose any body fat; he had only to pump up his muscles. His body responded quickly to weight training, and he had the intense psychological incentive of impending stardom in a major movie as a motivation. An unbeatable combination.

We all do not have such a strong incentive to help us speed our growth. It may take three months, six months, or even a year before you have achieved the shape you ultimately want. Many of us have the added burden of losing fat while building muscle. That approach-avoidance conflict acts as a confusing aspect for our psychological image and may keep us from shaping up as quickly as we'd like. Once the fat is gone, however, the muscles really seem to get going. That is partly because you can see them better without the camouflage of body fat. The excess fat acts as a drag on a muscle-building program, since you don't have as much energy to spare. And they actually grow faster once your body can devote more energy to them.

The basic programs in the previous chapters provide exercises that can be used indefinitely for shaping up as well as maintaining the body you build. Once you've reached your goal, you can continue to build up the intensity of the workouts, resulting in bigger muscles, or you can go on a maintenance type of workout schedule. At this point your muscles are ready for anything and are conditioned to grow or hold the line. If you stop working out altogether, however, the muscles will shrink.

To Hold the Line

If you want to maintain yourself at a certain level of development:

1. Keep the weights at the last level of resistance you were working with.

2. Do not work out three times a week every week. Alternate lifting weights twice a week with doing it three times a week. You may even skip a week here and there. If you find your muscles fighting a little harder to do the workout, then get back on the three-times-a-week schedule until you've regained your level of strength again.

You might increase the weights temporarily for a while to get a little ahead of yourself, then slack off again to allow a minimal amount of backsliding. The maintenance keeps your muscles at a fine line of balance through this kind of adjusting and gauging.

3. Some people use variations in sets and repetitions to maintain their development level. They go to the gym three times a week but more or less do sets with the weights—sometimes changing the weights as well—to keep their shape where they want it.

Vary the kind of exercises you do. For example, if you have been doing leg extensions and leg curls for your legs, you might switch over to using the leg-press machine. This exercises the same muscles but provides another dimension and works them in a different way. The use of various exercises for the same muscle groups is a very good practice all the way through.

Using varied exercises guarantees a full range of movement and development. Your muscles gain in strength for all types of movements instead of for just one. To use the thigh exercises as an example again:

■ The leg press requires you to use *all* the muscles of the thighs, hips, and buttocks at the same time.

■ The leg extension and leg curl work the muscles separately.

In your daily activities you will be climbing stairs—which calls for the leg-press kind of full-muscle strength—or performing a sport which might require you to use the front or back muscles of the thighs separately. From this point of view, it is best to alternate the types of weight-lifting exercises you do for the thighs so that you will be strong for all kinds of activities.

The same approach holds for the other muscle groups as well. Our muscles are capable of a very wide range of movement. There are hundreds of ways to lift weights in order to strengthen the basic muscle structure for all the ways you may need to use your body. If you are into mountain climbing, you will certainly want your arms to be conditioned to pull you up—as you would get through pulldowns with weighted pulleys. And you will want your legs to have the flexibility and strength needed for long reaches and the ability to follow through pulling you up from one point to another.

Obviously, for this kind of specialized activity, leg extensions and curls will not be as good for the conditioning required as leg presses and stretching.

When you get past the point of being a novice at weight training, you can branch out and apply the principles you've learned in order to bring new types of exercises into your regimen that will serve your own lifestyle requirements.

To Keep Building

You may decide you want to go for the big muscles after you've been in a weight-training program for a while. The basic program here is a good launching pad. All other exercises are simply variations. To get into bigger muscles, you can incorporate several approaches and use each one. The point of bodybuilding is to work with all methods and all exercises at ever-increasing weights and repetitions.

1. Keep adding weights and sets of repetitions as you progress.

2. Add different types of exercises for the same muscle groups instead of sets for the same exercise.

Example: You would do leg extensions and curls for a full complement of sets. You would also do another full complement of leg presses on the same day. You would follow the same practice for the other muscle groups—performing several sets of different types of exercises for each.

No matter how much you grow, the basic principles you learned at the outset remain unchanged as you build up your regimen. You can still hurt a muscle by not using the weights correctly even years after you've been weight-training.